Cups & Sauces

Chemo Cookery Club

Cups & Sauces

Breast Cancer Edition

Penny Ericson & Barbara Parry MSc RD

Exercise – Sarah Gibbings

Hair, nail & skincare – Ian Carmichael MVO

Acknowledgements

Chemo Cookery Club has turned out to be a project, not just a book. Soon after its publication in 2013, I wrote a special breast cancer edition, *Around the Kitchen Table* for the Human Health Care team of Eisai EMEA. It was translated into German, Italian, French and Russian and the Eisai team made it available free to tens of thousands of breast cancer patients, carers and professionals across Europe and beyond. I owe a very special thank-you to Cressida Robson who made it such a success. She is the godmother of *Cups & Sauces.*

Our *Around the Kitchen Table* road shows gave us the opportunity to travel the UK meeting patients and professionals and listen to their stories. It didn't take long before our events incorporated a holistic approach incorporating specialist exercise, hair and skin care. For their professional expertise, commitment and contributions, a million thanks to Sarah Gibbings and Ian Carmichael MVO. The addition of fitness and wellbeing has made *Cups & Sauces* something so much better.

A very special thank-you to Dick Rainsbury FRCS for contributing his experience and wisdom. His talent as a surgeon and dedication to empower women with the courage and freedom to make their own choices when faced with radical surgery is unparalleled.

There is a very special group of ladies that deserve our deepest thanks. Janet Taylor, co-founder and Kay Alsop, manager of The Pink Place Cancer Charity (registered charity no 1153494) in Basingstoke, Hampshire and our exercise ladies – Maureen Brailey, Brenda Carrington, Sylvia Holland, Barbara Hutton, Yvonne Houston, Cheryl Howard, Ann Knight, Pam Love, Pam Monger, Lyn Nelson, Natasha Walsh and Chris Whiffin.

Finally, to our CCC team – Barbara and I couldn't get through it all without your enthusiasm, contributions and support. Thank-you to everyone that read and re-read the manuscript, tested recipes and gave invaluable feedback: Simon Hawkins, Mary Ericson, David Luscombe, Rupert Radcliffe-Genge, Juliet & John Alexander, Barbara Thomson, Tenzo Patricia Dravis Greene, Jane Johnston & David Mairs, Gayna Healy, Josh Lucas, Guy & Bridget Mainwaring-Burton, Jennie & Peter Bankes, David Blake and a very special thanks to Mark Pollock and Ben Delamere, who are always caring for the carers.

First published in paperback in 2020

ISBN: 978-0-9565771-4-6

British Library Cataloguing-in-Publication Data: A catalogue record for this book is available from the British Library.

In memory of three extraordinary people

Dr Clodagh Murphy

Barry Hobson

Geoffrey Healy

They enriched so many in every

aspect of their lives

Making food special
not special food

Foreword

Dick Rainsbury FRCS

This book is a real gem. *Cups & Sauces* provides easily understandable, evidence-based guidance for patients, their families and friends, supporting them through their treatment. It also builds on the success of two forerunning books by Penny and Barbara, the original *Chemo Cookery Club* and *Around the Kitchen Table.*

The enjoyment of food is at the heart of these books. The range of dishes, tastes and choices reflects Penny's experience and skill in the kitchen as well as her first-hand experience as a carer. It equally brings Barbara's unique experience as the only dietitian in the South of England with a specialism in breast cancer. This book is another step along an exciting new road that encourages patients to take more control over their treatment and recovery, helping them to make important choices.

Patient choice has been a guiding principle throughout my life as a surgeon, and this has influenced many aspects of the approach our team takes to the diagnosis and management of people entrusted to our care. This same principle also inspired me to publish a book to help patients facing choices about breast reconstruction as part of their breast cancer surgery – *Breast Reconstruction – Your Choice**. Its text is based on the narratives of the women across the UK that faced difficult choices. They wanted to share their experiences and help others make their decisions based on evidence.

Survival from breast cancer has improved dramatically over the 30 years I've been a specialist in this field. Earlier diagnosis, better surgery, better drugs and better multidisciplinary care have all played their part, including an improved understanding of the vital role of lifestyle. There's much to celebrate but many questions remain unanswered and we've many challenges ahead.

So how can a cookery book and another about surgical treatment be similar? *Cups & Sauces* and *Breast Reconstruction – Your Choice* lie at opposite ends of the spectrum. At first glance, one is about lifestyle and the other about science but they share a common purpose. They share the goal to empower people and support them through one of the most difficult times of their lives. Penny and Barbara's new book will do much to help men and women with breast cancer to navigate that winding road back to health and wellbeing.

My own interest in diet and its impact on disease goes back a long way. It was triggered by Denis Burkitt when I was a medical student. Denis was a surgeon, scientist and epidemiologist. He was the first person to find a link between a virus and a cancer and he also provided fundamental evidence for a 'high-fibre diet' in the treatment for many ailments including: gallstones, diverticulitis, varicose veins and irritable bowel syndrome. Based on his groundbreaking observations in Uganda, he postulated that these diseases, which were rare in Africa, were actually caused by our Western diet. He also postulated that many cancers, including breast cancer, which was uncommon in Africa, developed as the result of the diets that dominate the Western World.

Denis Burkitt's intellect and research inspired me to explore the relationship between diet and breast cancer shortly after my appointment as a consultant breast surgeon in Winchester in 1987. Evidence at that time established a link between the risk of developing breast cancer and diet but the evidence supporting a role for diet in enhancing the outcomes of treatment was in its infancy.

I spent time in New York in the early 90s, learning about diet from a leading American epidemiologist, Dr Ernst Wynder. He launched a world first – a randomised prospective trial investigating the effect of a low fat dietary intervention on the outcomes of treatment for a group of women who had already developed early stage breast cancer. The first part of this trial was to show that women could actually stick to this diet for at least 2 years. Dr Wynder's team had demonstrated that it was possible for women in the US to maintain this diet given appropriate support but we had yet to show it was possible for women in the UK.

Securing research funding from the World Cancer Research Fund, UK, the Breast Cancer Research Trust and the Winchester Cancer Research Trust, we launched the *WINS (UK) – Stage 1 Study* in 2000. With considerable help from Barbara, we developed the methodology, materials and nutritional expertise to support this innovative study, to see it through to a successful conclusion. We were able to show that, with the right nutritional advice and support, women with breast cancer in the UK can achieve and maintain big changes in their diets.

Meanwhile back in the US, Dr Wynder and his colleagues were following up their breast cancer patients who had stuck to the diet. They compared their outcomes with a control group of survivors who had been given healthy eating advice and they were able to show for the first time that the women who had stuck to their diet experienced better outcomes.

So why are aspects of diet and other lifestyle factors becoming so important today in the treatment and support of the more than 50,000 women who develop breast cancer every year in the UK? The answer lies in our recognition that each person plays an important role in his or her treatment decisions and we now understand the fundamental importance of wellbeing, quality of life and choice for everyone experiencing this disease.

This is why Penny and Barbara stand out.

They recognise the diversity of people's experience from first-hand experience. Instead of saying, 'this is the way to do it', they suggest, 'you might like this'. They know the breadth of issues and treatment choices that women need to consider, in particular that:

- people have different preferences when it comes to their need for information. *Cups & Sauces* is a book you enjoy from cover-to-cover or you may prefer to just dip into it from time-to-time
- the information in *Cups & Sauces* can prompt a conversation with your specialist healthcare team about advice and support. Even though there are few dietitians that work exclusively within breast units in the UK, access to their expertise is a fundamental part of enhancing the outcomes of treatment
- making a good decision is a personal thing. Everyone's experience of breast cancer is different and the factors that inform our decisions about food, physical activity and appearance are equally unique. There isn't a one size fits all approach
- thinking about what's important to you can help put lifestyle changes into context It's more than just being aware of the evidence in favour of that change; it's also about finding practical ways to put that knowledge into practice and you'll find plenty of helpful suggestions here
- taking time to think about how the course of your treatment might affect you is important. At different stages of treatment, you may experience different effects on your food intake, physical activity and appearance and this book offers guidance at every stage.

A cancer diagnosis is an extremely emotional experience. How reassuring to have such expert guidance if you're unsure about anything. *Cups & Sauces* addresses a very real need and reflects the unique experience of each of its expert contributors. I'm delighted to recommend it to you.

Dick Rainsbury

**Breast Reconstruction – Your Choice*, Dick Rainsbury & Virginia Straker, 2008

A note to our readers

Making food special not special food

Penny Ericson

This book doesn't seek to offer specific dietary advice; rather it's a collection of ideas for people whose health and treatment have affected the daily pleasures of food. If you have any specific questions about what is best or appropriate for you, consult your dietitian or doctor.

Cups & Sauces has been produced, in its entirety, in a home kitchen. As such, things like cooking times, temperature controls and exact ingredient measurements may vary. The oven temperatures are given as ºCf, centigrade, fan-assisted, (see conversion chart, oven temperatures on page 331). My principles about ingredients and preparation are simple. The process is 'market to table in a day.' I think of each recipe as part of a day in the life of someone who lives on their own whilst undergoing treatment or for anyone who is responsible for the well-being of another. This means examining the manner in which people go about things, considering knowledge about food, energy levels, time management and availability of ingredients. In other words, not as professional chefs and medical professionals, but as mere mortals with the resources we have to hand.

For special dietary needs

Having a separate veggie section in the back of a cookery book has always seemed like a form of segregation. For me, food is about enjoyment whatever your preferences and dietary needs. The vegetarian dishes in this book are an integral part and appear throughout, they aren't separated.

When I prepare a menu for friends and family there's rarely any need to create a separate menu.

If gluten-free is required I prepare it for everyone at the table. Accommodating a special diet should be an extension of culinary creativity not an afterthought.

I've always wanted these books to be about everyday food that help people experiencing cancer treatment. If your medical advice or lifestyle requires a specialised diet, I encourage you to switch ingredients and also seek out information specific to your needs.

In keeping with our Chemo Cookery Club philosophy, we leave it you, the cooks and readers to make your own decisions. We have relied on the evidence-based information accepted by registered dietitians and nutrition specialist organisations including: Coeliac UK and Allergy UK.

Pastry

I've chosen to use store-bought short pastry, puff pastry and filo. Wherever possible the recipes are designed to ease complexity and deliver a great dish. This seemed like a natural shortcut. If you're a keen cook, I've included a classic short-crust recipe in *The basics & extras* on page 285.

Sauces and marinades

Here I have offered a mixture, some from scratch, others store bought. For example, I've given a recipe for Hollandaise sauce but you may find it easier to use store bought. Where I've included a recipe it's because the flavours are inherent to the dish. Store bought will alter the nutritional analysis, as they tend to be higher in salt, sugar and fats.

'Season to taste'

This generally means add salt and pepper to taste. When preparing dishes I season throughout the process and only when required as this enhances and balances flavour where seasoning only at the end can mask flavour or be too strong.

Pepper

This is black pepper unless otherwise specified. Typically, white pepper is used in cooking fish and sauces.

Salt

I have used Maldon sea salt flakes unless otherwise specified. If this is unavailable, a delicate 'fleur de sel' (also a fine sea salt) is a good substitute. Salts vary greatly in intensity so take care. Also, be aware of country variations in food legislation and labelling. In the UK, table salt is not iodized. In most EU countries and North America it is. Sea salt is naturally high in iodine. (Where possible, our nutritional analysis takes into consideration the levels of iodine in natural sea salt as the analysis software Dietplan is a UK nutrient database.)

Sriracha

This is a chilli sauce originally from Malaysia. Used judiciously it adds lift to sauces and marinades without the intense heat of other chilli sauces. It's great for bumping up flavour in response to loss of taste as the result of treatment. It is available in supermarkets and Asian grocery stores. For a bit more information about chilli paste and seasoning with chillies go to *The basics & extras*, page 285.

A word on wine, spirits and the use of alcohol

Some of the recipes in this book include alcohol as an ingredient. It's used to add and enhance flavour, for example, in a marinade or aperitif to 'tingle the tastebuds'.

In every instance, the recipes can be followed without the use of alcohol. Substitutes can be used, for example, using a juniper berry infusion to replace gin for the gin and tonic ice lollies. I leave it to you, the cook, to choose.

In general, the advice about drinking alcohol after a cancer diagnosis is expressed in terms of whether you've been a drinker in the past or not. If not then best not to start! If you have enjoyed a glass or three though, it's recommended that you have alcohol free days and try to keep to as little as possible when you do. Ideally, no more than 1 to 2 units and not every day, as alcohol is known to increase the risk of a number of cancers. Sound guidance and information is available on the World Cancer Research Fund (www.wcrf-uk.org) and American Institute for Cancer Research (www.aicr.org) websites.

Get ready for your treatment

There are a few things you can do to smooth the way if you have time. Such as:

- go to the dentist before treatment begins
- adjust your wardrobe so you've clothes that are comfortable and easy to get in and out of
- plan how your laundry will be done if you won't feel up to doing it
- arrange the rooms where you will spend most of your time so that they are easy to move around and have what you want, for example, a supply of bottled water next to the bed. Make them rooms you want to spend time in
- stock the loo with supplies like toothpaste, loo roll, towels, facecloths and air freshener
- if you are losing your hair or have a sensitive scalp, try covering your pillows with old T-shirts. It makes cleaning up much easier and it'll save your bedding
- remove temptation – clear out and restock the kitchen cupboards and fridge
- stock up on food and supplies you know you will need and enjoy. For example, pre-freeze fresh fruit for smoothies
- find out who your best support groups are for things like hair-loss and carers' support.

Some kitchen tools that are endlessly useful are a high-powered blender, food processor, hand blender and a slow cooker. A good supply of cling film and freezer bags and small storage containers are also good to have to hand.

Is it an allergy, sensitivity or intolerance?

'Being allergic' has become a catch phrase for just about every level of intolerance ranging from a way to say, 'I don't like it' to life-threatening anaphylaxis. When faced with a cancer diagnosis, it becomes more important to understand the differences. Below are descriptions of the three general categories of food intolerance as set out by the NHS and supported by allergyuk.org.

Allergy

A reaction produced by the body's immune system when exposed to a normally harmless substance.

Sensitivity

The exaggeration of the normal effects of a substance. For example, the caffeine in a cup of coffee may cause extreme symptoms, such as palpitations and trembling.

Intolerance

Where a substance causes unpleasant symptoms, such as diarrhoea, but does not involve the immune system. People with an intolerance to certain foods can typically eat a small amount without having any problems.

My thoughts on shortcuts

The spirit of this book is to make good food accessible using classic and traditional techniques when times aren't their best. If you fancy a recipe but the preparation seems daunting go and buy it ready-made then do the easy stuff like preparing fresh sauces and condiments.

Some sound principles and helpful hints

Positive associations

We enjoy food with all our senses so if one or two of them aren't working at optimum strength it helps to enhance the experience of the others. It's been said that we eat with our eyes. If you can, take time to make dishes beautiful. Allow aromas to fill the room. How often have we heard comfort associated with the smell of baked bread or bacon frying in a pan?

Get to know your high days and low days. Our memories can play powerful tricks. When you can, plan your menus so that you have your favourite meals when you are feeling well. Have simple foods on and just after treatment days. Enjoy them with loved ones and friends.

Succumb to your cravings. Your body might be telling you that you need something. Don't break the rules; if you crave chocolate and aren't meant to have it, think what it's rich in, such as potassium and try a banana instead. Variety and small portions taken regularly can help ward off nausea and fatigue.

When I began writing *Chemo Cookery Club* I wasn't surprised by the amount of nutritional information and advice available. It was literally everywhere. I was overwhelmed by the amount of conflicting opinions and contradictory published research. What I wanted to know first and foremost was which foods could I rely on to be known as helpful, healthy and in some cases cancer arresting and preventative. With that established I could use those foods as the foundation for the recipes. I needed an expert.

Chemo Cookery Club really came alive the day I met Barbara Parry, MSc RD, she has brought so much to this project. We affectionately call her contribution 'the science bits' and without them this would be just another recipe book. These are the 'bits' that give the book nutritional reliability and gravitas. Barbara's thoughts on the ingredients are based on her years of experience as a registered dietitian working in research, health promotion, clinical dietetics and her collaborations with colleagues within the global network of cancer research organisations. I hope you enjoy using this book as much as we have enjoyed making it.

Our approach to the treatment, management and recovery from cancer has advanced considerably since the first publication of *Chemo Cookery Club* in 2013. We have become much more aware. There is so much more information available to us through channels such as the medical community, support organisations and media. As a result, we felt compelled to include sections on exercise and mobility and hair, nail and skincare that is evidence-based and medically supported. We think that these sections significantly enhance the entire Chemo Cookery Club project, the very least of which is helping people think about their overall wellbeing and encouraging them to do something positive.

Best wishes

Contents

Cancer & food

What we know so far

Barbara Parry

Every ten years the World Cancer Research Fund (WCRF; UK) and the American Institute for Cancer Research (AICR) publish their international expert report *Food, Nutrition, Physical Activity and the Prevention of Cancer: a Global Perspective.* The report holds at its heart the provision of dietary guidance to populations and individuals based on high quality and reliable scientific research. That's not to say we know all there will ever be to know about the diet-breast cancer relationship but in the past five decades we've come an incredibly long way. Research has allowed us to be confident that diet and physical activity are of fundamental importance in preventing cancer and also have a central role to play both during treatment and afterwards. How well we tolerate and respond to treatment and our future health are all influenced by our food, nutrition and physical well-being.

When talking about breast cancer specifically, it's important to recognise its complexity. Many people experience a diagnosis but one person's breast cancer is not the same as the next. We know a lot about its risk factors and how to treat the different types of breast cancer that present with different hormone-sensitivities. Some are diagnosed before menopause and others after. Some are an obvious lump and others aren't. Some are found early in the disease process, some are more advanced, some respond to tablet treatments, some need chemo, some need radiotherapy - and so it goes on.

When it comes to breast cancer, we certainly know a lot about the intricate pieces and how they fit together but there are still gaps in what is a very complex jigsaw puzzle. With this in mind, *Cups & Sauces* is not designed to be all things to all people, nor does it attempt to be the sole source of nutritional advice. It's intended to help people, their families and friends find a way through the breast cancer tunnel with a reliable and evidence-based guiding light.

So what does the latest best evidence tell us?

The WCRF/AICR commitment to continuously updating the guidance for specific types of cancer ensures that the evidence around breast cancer is reviewed more frequently than once every ten years. In fact, there have been three continuous update reports published about food, nutrition, physical activity and breast cancer – one in 2010, another in 2014 and, the most recent *Global Perspective* report for all cancer sites was released in 2018. In summary, the key points are:

- around 40% of breast cancer cases (based on UK statistics) are preventable through healthy lifestyle changes
- being a healthy weight and as lean as possible without being underweight reduces risk of breast cancer developing

- being more active (at least 30 minutes moderate activity per day) is definitely beneficial; anything that gets your heart beating faster and makes you breathe more deeply - like brisk walking, bike riding or dancing
- it's a good idea to cut down on alcohol. We can find it all too easy to regularly indulge and the evidence is strongly in support of having no more than one standard drink daily with some alcohol-free days
- if you can breastfeed after having a baby, it's not only good for your baby's health but it can also help protect you against breast cancer.

Remember that there are many factors that influence our food choices – what we experienced growing up, significant people in our lives, our culture and traditions, our knowledge about foods and food preparation. Also, food is more than just the nutrients it provides. We use food to celebrate special occasions, to comfort us when we're feeling low, to show hospitality when we have people around. Taking these factors into account is an important part of tailoring the advice about food and nutrition to something that's relevant for you.

Food enjoyment is fundamental to a healthy way of eating – making changes that mean you find yourself eating foods you really don't like will mean you're making temporary, 'I'm on a diet', type changes with only short term benefits. Give yourself the goal of making gradual changes that not only help your weight to come down but help to keep it off when you reach your goal.

Weight gain during breast cancer treatment is actually very common – with perhaps as many as three in every four women diagnosed finding this happens. There are many reasons for this, including the physical and psychological responses to the treatment itself resulting in changes to what you're eating, the way you're eating, how your body uses the food and how much activity you feel able to do. If this weight gain is prevented the response to treatment is better and you are less likely to face other health problems in the future.

Sometimes it's not so much what we're eating but when, where, why, how and with whom – it's easy to be distracted and less conscious of how much we're eating when we're eating whilst doing something else. It is, after all, a very pleasing way to pass the time. Because food is generally abundant in the UK, we're often tempted to eat when our bodies don't really need food. Have you noticed the ever-increasing number of coffee shops in our town centres and the delectable food programmes on TV and food advertising generally? It makes us think we're in need of food when actually we're not.

Don't mistake thirst for hunger – treatment can often lead to dehydration as the result of a number of factors such as nausea and sickness, diarrhoea or simply not drinking enough water.

Try to be mindful of continually taking fluids – as always 'little and often' is best. A great way to control this is, when you feel hungry have a drink of water. If and when the hunger returns it is time to eat.

With *Cups & Sauces*, we on the Chemo Cookery Club team aim to offer anyone who experiences the shock of a cancer diagnosis a way to make ordinary food special – with taste tempting flavours and simple to follow recipes. Not all the recipes will suit everyone so find a few little gems and make them your own.

Our unique *Thumbs-up guide©* illustrates the nutritional information at a glance so you can easily decide if a dish will be helpful in meeting your dietary needs and food preferences.

Sometimes, a breast cancer diagnosis and treatment side-effects can cause loss of appetite and worrying weight loss when people simply don't feel like eating. With this in mind, we've provided a range of recipes to cover all possibilities. Some of them are packed full of nutrients and also a great source of calories in small portions, (nutrient dense and calorie dense). Others are nutrient dense but lower in calories for people wanting to control their weight. There is something for everyone!

Our unique Thumbs-up guide© to nutrition

The nutrition information accompanying the recipes is intended as general guidance and not as specialist medical advice. However, our Thumbs-up guide utilises UK food composition databases and purpose built dietary analysis software, Dietplan 6 & 7, Forestfield Software Ltd.

There are many factors that will influence the absolute nutrient content of foods, including food storage and growing conditions. Therefore, our nutritional analysis uses a generous point of reference. The thumbs-up scoring for recipes is based on a percentage of Reference Nutrient Intake (RNI) levels, and a 'reference person' has been assumed. Everyone's nutritional needs are different so demonstrating that the recipes are good sources of these nutrients and also being consistent in our approach is important. Your doctor and registered dietitian can help you tailor the advice to your specific needs.

When *Chemo Cookery Club* was first published in 2013, Penny's husband, Simon, was chosen as the reference person for RNI comparisons. He was then a 50-ish male of moderate occupational and recreational activity. Male RNI's are generally higher for nutrients than the female equivalent and this offers an approximation for any increased energy needs that people may have whilst going through treatment. As the RNI for iron is higher for women before the menopause than men, but breast cancer is more common after the menopause when iron requirements for women are lower, an average of the male and pre-menopause female RNI's has been used for assessing the iron contribution of the recipes. So, essentially, we've used a calculation that is likely to cover the majority of UK population needs without over-estimating the likely contribution each recipe will make to nutrient intake.

Special provision has not been made for children's needs or pregnancy but you can be sure that these recipes will tempt the tastebuds at any age and they all lend themselves to adaptation and the use of substitute ingredients if required.

If a particular nutrient is not listed in the *Thumbs-up guide*© beside a recipe, this simply means that a portion provides less than 20% of the RNI. Many of the recipes will make a contribution to more than the nutrients listed but the thumbs-up scoring is formulated as follows:

Range	Score
> 100%	>👍👍👍👍
80 - 100%	👍👍👍👍
60 - 79%	👍👍👍
40 - 59%	👍👍
20 - 39%	👍
1 - 19%	no thumbs but may at times be credited for other value.

The RNI is the amount of a nutrient sufficient to ensure that the needs of nearly all the population (97.5%) are being met. Individual nutritional needs vary widely. Our figures are based on the UK population, not individuals. For further information about RNI visit www.foodafactoflife.org.uk.

Specialist advice

Our recipes are designed to be versatile and flexible. If you've been advised by your specialist to avoid eating some foods during treatment and one of them appears as an ingredient, simply substitute an alternative. If an ingredient is something you have a personal distaste for, again, change it to something you like. Bear in mind that cancer treatment can do strange things to your tastebuds, so flavours and textures you haven't enjoyed in the past may end up becoming your new favourite foods.

About our Libran scale ⚖

We have used this symbol to indicate where a recipe may provide plenty of nutrients but is actually less than 300 kcals per portion. This makes the recipe particularly suitable for people who are concerned about weight gain during and after treatment.

A week in the headlines

THE SUNDAY TIMES
Diet fights cancer
28 October

DAILY EXPRESS
Ban bacon say cancer experts
31 October

The Daily Telegraph
Red meat and alcohol increase cancer risk
1 November

THE Sun
Save our bacon: butty battle
1 November

THE TIMES
New rules for defeating cancer
1 November

Daily Mail
Is anything safe to eat?
1 November

the guardian
Blame it on the bacon
2 November

THE INDEPENDENT
Warning: scientist's advice about diet .... a recipe for confusion
4 November

London Evening Standard
Keep eating the bacon butties!
4 November

Myth busters

You can't always believe what you read in the papers!

Cancer has affected everyone in some way – either we've gone through it ourselves or we know someone who has. Experience is a great teacher but it's so important to remember that everyone's experience is unique.

We hear the words 'breast cancer' and we assume everyone has the same type of disease but this isn't the case. There are different types of breast cancer and, over the last two decades in particular, research into the role of food, nutrition and physical activity as part of treatment has revealed some important ways in which people can play an active part in promoting their future health.

At Chemo Cookery Club, the team has always been passionate about the unique focus of our books – putting real people and the issues they find important at the heart of our publications. We also want to ensure our advice is reliable, evidence-based and complementary to the advice your specialist health team provides.

We're not about preaching the 'do this and don't do that' messages. We're all about recognising the many factors that influence individual food choices, how much physical activity you feel able to do and how you feel about your appearance. We're partners in your journey through cancer treatment and want to help you find a way through that works for you. We don't want you making changes that are based on fear or hearsay or that sap your confidence in the gold standard healthcare available to you. We want to put enjoyment, reassurance and, wherever possible, clarity at the heart of the practical guidance we offer.

The amount of information available about cancer, research breakthroughs, treatment, new life sustaining treatment and medicines, holistic therapy and lifestyle choices is simply staggering. It's also often contradictory and confusing. Over the years, as we've talked with people going through treatment, their carers and loved ones, there are a number of recurring questions so we decided to include some of the 'big issues' in this edition.

Myth 1: Breast cancer is an exclusively female cancer

Perhaps this is the most important place to start; to acknowledge that one in every hundred diagnoses is male breast cancer. Because it is a much rarer condition, research into male breast cancer is less commonly included in review papers that describe the evidence for diet's role in management. Nevertheless, the importance of good nutrition to the outcome of treatment and food and the role of activity in promoting future health are unquestioned.

So, the take home message is breast cancer can occur in both men and women.

Myth 2: Any study can be used to show what causes cancer, as long as it's scientific

If you're not used to hearing it, the use of scientific language can seem impressive and convincing but you can't assume that all studies are the same, nor is scientific evidence always reported correctly. There is a temptation to assume that all studies have a 'cause' remit to show that 'x is caused by y'. 'Association', shown by observational studies, including cross-sectional, case-control and cohort studies, is not the same as 'cause', shown by experimental studies, like clinical trials. So, many scientific studies can only show associations. It's only the gold standard 'randomised controlled trial (RCT) that can truly show *X* is caused by *Y*.

When scientific papers report, '*There was a positive statistical association found between eating vegetables like cauliflower and broccoli (cruciferous vegetables) and the risk of certain cancers*', the media tend to 'over-report', so an association-based advancement in research can result in a seemingly spectacular headline like, *'Cauliflower cures cancer'!*

To understand more about the different types of scientific studies and what they can tell us, have a look at the World Cancer Research Fund (UK) and American Institute for Cancer Research websites.

Meanwhile, the take home message is all types of scientific study can help our understanding but not all scientific studies are equal.

Myth 3: I need to avoid dairy after a breast cancer diagnosis

A lot has been written about the relationship between dairy products and breast cancer and it is widely believed that there is a direct link. Existing evidence tells us that there is no strong association between the consumption of dairy foods and the risk of breast cancer. Also we know that'hormones and growth factors that may be detectable in very small quantities in milk do not survive the digestive process well.

We all recognise the planet's population is increasing and this means an increasing demand for food. Intensive agricultural practices have made us doubt the safety of our food supply. After any health scare, confidence in the foods we eat can fall or change as we are desperate to know why this has happened to us... and we tend to blame ourselves and how we eat. Searching the internet and other sources, including friends with personal experience can be supportive and helpful but also confusing as everyone's cancer and experience is different.

Agricultural legislation also differs from country to country. So it's really important to know if it is relevant to foods sold in the UK. Also, EU regulation of farming practices and food safety is reassuringly strict, much more so than in some other western countries and you should always confirm the country of source for the information you are reading.

It's also important to have just enough but not an excessive amount of these foods so that their nutritional contribution doesn't exceed your needs. Excessive amounts of high fat dairy foods can affect weight gain and this can have an effect on your treatment and overall well-being. Ask a registered dietitian to provide you with further information about your requirements for the important nutrients that dairy foods contain.

Myth 4: I need to give up processed foods and eat superfoods instead

In the first instance, we need to make sure we know what is meant by processed. Some preparation of foods, including peeling and chopping and blanching (part cooking before freezing), can be considered processing but it's also a time saving method of preparing and preserving good food from scratch.

Technically tinned foods are processed and some of that processing may involve the addition of salt, sugar and additives. Baked beans are a great example. Most people don't make them anymore. The tinned version is a well-loved staple in many households. They can be an important source of nutrition when you just fancy something quick and simple after a long day at the hospital. Also, marmalade is a processed food, as are breakfast cereals and everything that comes in a bag or box! This doesn't automatically make them carcinogenic or cancer promoting.

If you have concerns about the cautionary advice of processed meats and cancer risk, it really is best to ask your specialist dietitian and determine if your level of consumption warrants adjustment. You might use them at times when your tastebuds have dwindled and you need to give a dish a boost of flavour but you wouldn't necessarily be eating them all the time and in large amounts.

As for the term *superfoods*, this has become a *super* marketing term to encourage us to consider buying some new and perhaps *nutritionally interesting* foods, (of itself not a bad thing). Food labelling legislation in the UK generally prohibits health claims being made by food manufacturers. Often a so-called superfood is a particularly good source of a topical nutrient or other naturally occurring food chemical like glucosinolates or phytoestrogens so when a food marketing company wants its product to hit media headlines they shout, *'Superfood'*. On their own, they cannot ensure you're eating in a healthy way. In fact, if you relied solely on super foods you couldn't eat a healthy and balanced diet and you'd be missing out on a great deal of nutrition, not to mention food enjoyment.

So here's to super ways of eating and let's celebrate the wide variety of foods available to us that can encourage our eating patterns to be super sources of nutrition.

Myth 5: Eating foods labelled organic ensures that I am eating in a healthy way

Whilst the term 'organic' requires that certain legislative quality and other technical standards are met in the food and farming industries, it doesn't guarantee a nutritionally superior eating pattern.

The Department for Environment, Food & Rural Affairs (DEFRA), describes organic food as the product of a farming system which avoids the use of man-made fertilisers, pesticides, growth regulators and livestock feed additives. Irradiation and the use of genetically modified organisms, (GMOs), or products produced from or by GMOs are generally prohibited under organic legislation. Organic certification does, however, vary from country to country but if sold in the UK it must be compliant with EU legislation that currently defines the organic food labelling requirements for UK sales. A food can be labelled 'organic' only if at least 95% of its ingredients meet the necessary standards.

There is emerging evidence to show that there is a difference in nutritional composition between organic and conventionally grown produce. There are, however, many different factors that influence the nutrient variability of foods we eat, not just the agricultural practices which initially produce the foods. More research is needed to determine if eating organic food actually reduces cancer risk and to date, no studies have been undertaken to show a benefit to eating organic foods after a cancer diagnosis.

Food is more than a source of nutrition

Perception of risk

Readiness to change

Of course, people may choose organic foods for more than just nutritional reasons and may also choose not to eat organic foods if they find them too expensive or there is a lack of availability of organic foods in their local supermarket.

(Some farms in the UK were stripped of their organic status when the legislation moved from the UK to the EU because they didn't meet the broader set of pan-EU rules. The message is, foods from local farmers, markets and other local sources can be just as good without an 'organic' label. Get to know where your food comes from).

Myth 6: Weight gain during treatment is a good thing

Weight gain during treatment is very common, as many as 3 in every 4 women experience it during the first year after diagnosis. It is often assumed that after a cancer diagnosis, weight gain is reassuring because weight loss is more commonly the result of both the disease and treatment.

BUT for those experiencing breast cancer we have known for nearly three decades that weight gain is not a good thing. If your weight puts you outside the healthy range for your height, there's an increased amount of circulating oestrogen, (from body fat stores), an increased risk of breast cancer coming back and you're at risk of other diseases in later life including heart disease and diabetes.

Being a healthy weight and aware that weight gain during treatment is best avoided means that you're helping to make your specialist treatment as effective as possible and taking a very positive step towards staying healthy in the future. Exercise and activity are the best partners for a balanced diet.

Myth 7: Grapefruit, being an acid food, will promote the growth of cancer

Grapefruit is often a food that hits the headlines and for apparently conflicting reasons.

During cancer treatment, you may be advised to avoid certain foods, drinks, medicines and supplements because of the possibility of them interfering with your prescribed treatment. It's important for your specialist team to know that the prescribed medicines for your treatment don't have their action interrupted or impaired by other things that your digestive system is handling at the same time.

We know that grapefruit, grapefruit juice and some exotic fruits contain a substance that blocks some of the enzymes produced in the liver and small intestine, called 'cytochrome P enzymes'. There are also herbal supplements that affect these enzymes but your specialist team will be able to tell you if you need to avoid or limit these foods and supplements during treatment.

In 2012, there was a headline declaring that *'grapefruit juice improves cancer medication'*, suggesting that patients only needed about a third of their cancer treatment drug to achieve *'optimal cancer-fighting levels'*. This type of study was actually exploring 'pharmacokinetic modulators', including food-drug interactions but importantly this was a study of patients with advanced brain and blood cancers and the conclusions stated that the effect of the grapefruit juice was variable and not precise enough to allow doctors to use this interaction in the calculation of a prescribed dose without putting patients through gut enzyme testing.

Grapefruit contains citric acid and is considered acidic by proponents of diets that try to modify the body's pH. As research has progressed to understand the environment in which cancer cells multiply and how this might be altered to disrupt the process, there has been interest in the so-called *alkaline diet* that claims to alter the body's pH and provide an environment that prohibits the growth of cancer cells.

Whilst it is true to say that cancer cells favour anaerobic metabolism and produce lactic acid as a by-product that causes the immediate environment outside each cancer cell to be acidic, cancer cells, like many other cells, maintain a pH of around 7.4 within each cell. This is the same as the pH of the blood and virtually neutral, (neither alkaline nor acidic). The body's pH is very effectively controlled using normal body functions including our breathing (respiration) and urine excretion via the kidneys. Diet cannot affect the pH of the body nor can it alter the pH around a tumour. Some cancer cells multiply in acidic environments and some in alkaline environments. Further, when you actually calculate the potential renal acid load (PRAL) of foods to indicate an acidic or an alkaline effect, citrus fruits produce an alkaline result (negative PRAL). So, by this physiologically relevant classification, grapefruit is not acidic at all!

Myth 8: Phytoestrogens will cause my oestrogen-sensitive (ER positive) cancer to return

What we eat really is a chemistry lesson! The term phytoestrogen is becoming as familiar to the general population as the term omega 3 fatty acid and carbohydrate. These are terms that derive their names from a system of naming chemicals when they are naturally present in foods and also the result of food processing as something added in food manufacture. So, phytoestrogens are similar (but not identical) in their chemical structure to the hormone, oestrogen (17ß-oestradiol) but found naturally in plant-derived foods and drinks.

Phytoestrogens have been shown to have anti-oxidant effects and, in the normal concentrations found in whole foods, are more likely to have an anti-oestrogenic effect than increasing total oestrogen exposure. Although different types of phytoestrogens have different effects, they are generally much less 'oestrogenic', (less potent), than the hormone oestrogen. There is some evidence that certain phytoestrogens have the capacity to bind to oestrogen receptors thereby blocking the effects of any circulating 17ß-oestradiol. Human studies about the effects of dietary consumption amongst the diversity of the foods we eat have yet to directly explore this complexity in enough detail to draw definitive conclusions on breast cancer outcomes.

Rest assured that the food sources of phytoestrogens are also some of the best sources of other essential nutrients in our eating patterns and, in those healthy whole food quantities, it's unlikely that any harmful effects will be seen.

Myth 9: I need to avoid sugar because it feeds cancer

Again, this is an attention grabber when it hits the headlines and, whilst there is some science behind the statement, it is mostly viewed in isolation from other considerations that are so important to achieving appropriate nutritional intake during and after cancer treatment.

Yes, cancer cells preferentially use glucose, derived from many dietary sources of carbohydrate, both sugars and starches, but so do other cells. Deprive the cancer cells and you deprive the healthy cells in the body too.

Cancer cell biology is more than just the increased rates of using glucose and producing lactic acid, there is also activation of oncogenes, activation or suppression of growth factor pathways and 'escape from apoptosis', (the normal cycle of cell death doesn't occur in cancer cells). It's not something driven by dietary sources of carbohydrate.

Certainly if there is the need to control energy (calorie) intake, limiting highly refined carbohydrate, particularly added sugars, can be beneficial but there are also times when it can be nutritionally beneficial to concentrate nutrients and calories in a smaller volume of food when appetite is poor (see page 246, introduction to section *Something Sweet – Puddings*).

Whilst there may be some suggestions in the scientific literature that restricting carbohydrate is beneficial, (from studies of very hard to treat cancers, like glioblastoma for example), it's important to remember evidence is still very limited and poor quality nutritional intake even nutritional deficiencies are a likely outcome.

Myth 10: Taking supplements is the best way to get the nutrients I need

With very few exceptions, whole foods are the best way to get the nutrients you need. People who take dietary supplements tend to be those in least need of them because they are usually already conscious of their nutritional intake.

There is no evidence that taking dietary supplements enhances the outcomes of cancer treatment, with the possible exception of vitamin D.

It's early days in our understanding of the relationship between vitamin D status and the outcomes of breast cancer treatment but there is some emerging evidence of possible benefits. There is an increased recognition of the importance of our vitamin D status to our general health and living in countries like the UK, where summers are short and winters are long, it seems reasonable to at least aim for the recommended daily intake of 10ug (400IU).

The best dietary sources of Vitamin D include oily fish, eggs, fortified breakfast cereals and wild mushrooms, but they are not always sufficient to maintain the body's vitamin D status without some sunlight exposure. Being physically active outdoors can enhance our vitamin D status but actually taking a 10ug daily supplement can be a reassurance, particularly during the winter months.

Cups & Sauces is here to give you confidence in food, showing you how everyday ingredients can provide a great source of nutrition to help you through treatment and promote your health for the future.

Friendly foods

Wouldn't it be grand if food could definitively prevent or cure cancer. Alas, it isn't so – not yet!

The right foods can, however, lower the risk of developing the disease, aid in treatment and promote your physical and psychological health and wellbeing. Many foods contain natural food chemicals such as antioxidants that help reduce the tendency for cancer cells to develop and we are beginning to understand how phytochemical compounds like isothiocyanates protect cells from the disease. The emerging evidence is exciting.

Cancer doesn't appear overnight. It takes time to develop and cancer isn't just one simple disease but rather a group of more than one hundred diseases, all of which involve cells growing out of control as a result of changes in the genetic information in those cells. There are several ways in which food can disrupt the cancer process. We know that eating in a healthy way can benefit quality of life during treatment and afterwards. So, good food and a healthy lifestyle is a 'win-win'.

Nutrition and physical activity can influence cancer development and progression in a number of ways, including: DNA repair, hormone regulation, inflammation and immunity, cancer cell metabolism, proliferation, differentiation and cell death. If you'd like to know more about these complex processes in the body, the World Cancer Research Fund (UK) and American Institute for Cancer Research are both sources of great information and can help you learn more about how nutrition can help.

The way food tastes is important but we also eat with our eyes. In many instances, the best nutrition comes from the very components that give food its colour. It seems nature intended wellness to be bold and bright. Whenever possible, choose foods that are in season and as fresh as they can be. Locally sourced foods have often travelled shorter distances from field-to-shopping basket and so may be better sources of nutrients, particularly if prepared in a way that will preserve those water-soluble and heat sensitive ones.

There is evidence that certain food types and food preparation methods can contribute to cancer development, so be aware of things like chargrilling, barbequing and certain types of curing where nitrites are produced in the foods. Of course, the flavours that these processes add might be just what you need, in small quantities, when your tastebuds need tingling so it's a matter of getting the balance right. During treatment, meals can taste bland, or weirdly metallic as a result of medication side-effects so sometimes strong flavours are just what you need to get through these times.

It might be helpful to use a probiotic supplement if your treatment results in digestive problems such as diarrhoea or abdominal discomfort as a result of flatulence. Probiotics are a source of 'friendly bacteria' that can help replace the natural bacteria in your gut and aid digestion. However, everybody's gut is populated with different types of bacteria and some specialist advice will be helpful. Be mindful that cancer treatment can reduce your white blood cell count, known as neutropenia and if so, you may be advised to avoid foods and drinks (including probiotics, live and bio products, uncooked foods, even ordinary tap water) to reduce your risk of developing a food or water-borne infection.

Here are a few of the foods highlighted in this book, that have been shown to be beneficial. Why not make them your new best friends.

Alliums – garlic & onions, leek & chives

Alliums are truly amazing vegetables and include those flavour powerhouses, onions and garlic. Laboratory studies show that they contain sulphur compounds that can help slow or stop tumour cell growth and these vegetables continue to be studied for their protective effects against cancers. We're gradually learning how even the humble onion can be a dietary super hero. It's already a great ingredient that features in many *Cups & Sauces* recipes alongside its cousins, garlic, chives and leeks.

Avocados

Just one avocado contains one quarter of the adult recommended daily amount of potassium and provides a rich source of a number of nutrients that can act as antioxidants and attack free radicals in the body. It makes a delicious toast topper for a savoury breakfast or snack and you won't need to worry about spreading butter or margarine first because it'll be a naturally creamy topping without. Guacamole is an easy light snack, great at any time – (see page 105).

Beans, legumes & pulses

Lentils, peas, chickpeas, soya, fava and other varieties of beans are full of phytochemicals found naturally in plants. They are also a great source of fibre that helps our digestive system get rid of waste efficiently, thereby flushing through things that may be harmful to our health. This is one of the reasons why beans and other fibre-rich foods are associated with a reduced risk of bowel cancer. Beans are also a great source of protein and a really good source of iron, (especially when eaten with foods or drinks that are a good source of vitamin C; vitamin C enhances the absorption of iron from plant foods).

Soya beans, in particular, contain 'isoflavones' which are naturally occurring oestrogen-like chemicals that may block breast tumour growth. Lentils and peas are wonderfully versatile and full of flavour. Chickpeas make a great snack as they come, or can be made into hummus – (see page 87).

Beetroot

Beetroot and other purple foods such as red cabbage, aubergine and red grapes contain anthocyanins that have been shown in laboratory studies to interrupt cancer cell growth and so contribute to cancer cell death.They're also rich in cancer-fighting flavonoids that have antioxidant and anti-inflammatory properties, creating a more favourable environment for healthy cells to thrive. After you've eaten a lot of beetroot, don't be alarmed if your wee turns pink! Add beetroot to salads or make a visually stunning beetroot risotto – (see page 211). Yummy!

Berries

Like beetroot, berries are colourful fruits that are high in fibre and vitamin C. There are so many varieties to enjoy – cherries, cranberries, raspberries, blackberries, blueberries, strawberries, loganberries, and tayberries – the list goes on! Great eaten on their own or added to brighten a meal. How much more delicious is the simplest of fruit salads thanks to the addition of a handful of berries. Start the day with a berry smoothie or try frozen berry compote – (see page 53).

Carrots

Carrots are orange in colour because of the carotene they contain. Carotene is one of a group of naturally occurring chemicals – carotenoids, which are antioxidants. Raw carrots are also a source of falcarinol that researchers suggest may slow the growth of cancer cells. Carrots are super as a snack on their own. They're also marvellous julienned and added to any stir-fry as they hold their shape and texture and add the perfect contrast to a green medley. Apricots, squash and sweet potatoes are also a good source of carotenoids. Orange just became one of my favourite colours!

Cruciferous vegetables – broccoli, Brussels sprouts, bok choi, cabbage, cauliflower & kale

These beautiful vegetables contain chemicals called glucosinolates that when digested are broken down into isothiocyanates and indoles. In laboratory and human studies, all of these are demonstrating beneficial effects for cancer prevention. Raw broccoli is higher in calcium, vitamins A and C, than milk and oranges. As we usually eat broccoli cooked, the heat sensitive and water-soluble nutrients such as vitamin C and calcium can be diminished. We're still learning how powerful these wonderful veggies truly are. Try crudites with tzatziki and hummus – (see pages 87 & 110). Delicious!

Eggs

Eggs provide us with the highest quality dietary protein, readily providing us with the essential amino acids that our bodies aren't able to manufacture. The fat profile of eggs varies according to the diet of the hens that lay them. The fat is found exclusively in the yolk. Eggs are also a good source of folic acid and riboflavin (B-group vitamins) as well as the antioxidant trace mineral selenium. Eggs can be prepared to be either savoury or sweet dishes and are easy to eat and digest, perfect for a light meal after a busy treatment day.

Mushrooms

Mushrooms are a particularly good source of the B Group vitamins riboflavin (vitamin B2), niacin (vitamin B3) and pantothenic acid (vitamin B5) as well as the minerals copper and selenium. Some people just can't get their heads around the texture of mushrooms. If you're one of them, try not to pass the little belters by. Added as a purée to sauces they don't have to overpower other ingredients and all the goodness is still there. Wild mushrooms are an important source of vitamin D, another nutrient that is emerging in scientific literature as being important to the outcomes of cancer treatment?

Oily fish & flax seed

As a source of omega-3 fats these are unequalled.

Oily fish such as herring, mackerel and salmon are important sources of vitamin A, selenium and vitamin D as well as omega-3 fats. Oily fish, (in fact, fish in general), is also a good source of protein and naturally low in saturated fats. Worldwide, there are concerns about the toxic chemicals that can accumulate in fish resulting from the pollution of our oceans and rivers. Heavy metal toxicity, eg mercury, is a particular concern. Further, certain fishing methods are environmentally destructive which may discourage us from choosing fish as part of our regular eating pattern. Take care in sourcing your fish and shellfish, buy from stockists that have a clear sustainability policy. We've been advised for many years to include oily fish two to three times per week for a healthy heart and to reduce risk of stroke but it is emerging as important for cancer prevention as well. Omega-3 fats have been shown through laboratory studies to reduce inflammation and encourage the synthesis of prostaglandins; both processes disrupt the cancer process. Salmon from well-managed fisheries, sardines, farmed rainbow trout, barramundi, farmed mussels and other shellfish are likely to have lower levels of environmental toxins but it is always a good idea to ask your fish supplier for more information.

Flax seed is the best plant source of omega-3 fats but the jury is still out as to whether it has a role to play in cancer prevention. While it can boost your intake of magnesium, manganese, selenium, thiamine (vitamin B1) and dietary fibre, it may also interfere with the absorption of some medicines. Using one to four tablespoons per day appears to be safe but really it is probably 'one to watch' until more is known about its biological effects.

Peppers & jalapenos

Peppers (capsicums) are a top source of vitamin C, especially when eaten raw. Chilli peppers such as jalapenos contain a chemical called capsaicin that is being studied further as it has been shown to interrupt cancer cell growth in laboratory studies. Capsaicin is the very ingredient that makes chillies hot and might be just the thing to give a zing to your tastebuds during treatment.

Seeds & nuts

Seeds and nuts such as pumpkin, sunflower and sesame seeds, almonds and walnuts are the most concentrated sources of plant protein and also contain other nutritional goodies such as potassium, magnesium, zinc, vitamin E, iron, B vitamins and dietary fibre. Zinc helps vitamin C do its job so healthy levels can improve healing time. Zinc also plays an important role in how well our tastebuds work, (we lose our taste sensitivity if we become deficient in zinc), so enjoying foods that provide us with zinc could help rev-up a flagging appetite too.

Some seeds and nuts can be a non-dairy source of calcium as well. Being such a powerhouse of nutrition, (after all, seeds can be the source of many a thriving new plant in the vegetable garden), they can boost your intake of nutrients even when only small amounts are eaten. While some people argue that peanuts are not truly nuts, peanut butter has to be one of the best comfort foods that delivers so much in such a friendly way. Have it on toast or try it with banana in a smoothie, particularly if your appetite's gone off the boil.

Spices – Turmeric, black pepper & more

There is emerging evidence of how herbs and spices may be of benefit in cancer prevention. Of course, the practice of using them as treatment goes back millennia and exists today in every culture. If for no other reason, herbs and spices give us flavour, texture and aroma. Good news for curry fans. *Cups & Sauces* uses herbs and spices to delight the taste buds. They are used in small quantities so we have chosen not to focus on their medicinal potential but we are hearing more and more in the scientific review of food's medicinal effects that there are antioxidant, anti-inflammatory, anti-microbial and anti-nausea properties from these friendly flavouring agents.

Spinach & watercress

Dark green, leafy vegetables are great sources of vitamin A, vitamin K, dietary fibre, folate and carotenoids, all with potential cancer fighting properties. Perhaps it's the folate they contain that makes them most interesting. Folate is important for producing and maintaining healthy DNA that carries each cell's reproduction code. An error in the code means a mistake in the healthy division and reproduction of cells that starts the cancer process in the body.

Watercress is a rich source of the glucosinolate, gluconasturtin (phenethylglucosinolate) and is allied to the cruciferous friendly foods we referred to earlier. Research is gradually helping us to understand why diets rich in such vegetables actually lower cancer risk. In 2013, for example, an extract of watercress has been shown to disrupt the process by which breast cancer cells maintain their blood supply. Without a blood supply to carry nutrients and oxygen to them, cancer cells can't survive or reproduce, which is great news!

Tomatoes

Tomatoes are rich in lycopene, an antioxidant that tackles those free radicals that are part of the process that triggers cancer cell growth. Also found in some other vegetables and fruits, lycopene is actually best absorbed after cooking and is the most potent carotenoid antioxidant. Studies have shown lycopene to improve immune function, reduce inflammation and proliferation of cancer cells and even lower LDL (bad) cholesterol. Tomatoes are also rich in vitamin C, which is most abundant when raw. As variety is the spice of life, enjoy tomatoes raw, cooked and often.

Water

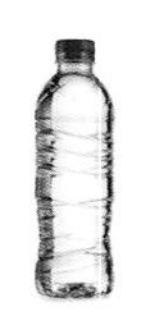

Well, it isn't exactly food but it cannot be ignored. Dehydration is an often over looked symptom and relief is easy. Remember to drink. Little and often. Flavour it, chill it, and freeze it. Keep it with you. It is also important not to misread thirst as hunger as this can lead to undesirable weight gain and the solution might be just a glass of water away.

Whole grain

Perhaps a good place to start is by describing just what is meant by 'whole grain'. There are three distinct parts to plant grains; the germ, containing vitamin E and other antioxidant nutrients plus some fat; the endosperm, containing predominantly starchy carbohydrate with some B vitamins and some protein; the bran, a potent source of dietary fibre and other vitamins, minerals and nutrients, many with antioxidant properties. Whole grain and wholemeal are terms that we sometimes use interchangeably but when it comes to the type of bread we buy or bake, we tend to think of whole grain as a granary-type while wholemeal is the smooth one. Granary bread is not to everyone's taste and you'll still find the wholemeal varieties make a better contribution to your nutrition than a white loaf. Having said that, a plain old white loaf has its place, especially if things are delicate in the large bowel department.

Whole grains are known to play an important role in prevention of cancers of the lower digestive tract and research continues to demonstrate cancer-specific and other health benefits. There is also evidence of benefits in reducing breast cancer risk. Enjoy any grain-derived food whether it be a variety of bread, breakfast cereal, starchy grain, rice, polenta, cous cous or pasta and favour those labelled wholemeal or whole grain whenever you can for an extra boost to your nutrient intake. Whole grains are a great source of iron and B vitamins as well.

Yoghurt & probiotics

Yoghurt is a light, nutrient-packed food that's so versatile it can be used in the main course and then again for dessert! You can 'turn down the heat' in a curry by adding natural yoghurt but 'turn up the nutrition' because it's a great source of calcium, protein, B-group vitamins and can also be a source of 'friendly' bacteria. A side-effect of treatment can be disruption to the normal balance of friendly bacteria in the digestive tract causing such problems as bloating, flatulence, abdominal cramps or diarrhoea. While everyone's mix of digestive bacteria is different, it's important to maintain the balance for healthy digestion and absorption of nutrients and to form part of the 'first line of defence' to protect the body from disease.

The Food and Agriculture Organisation/World Health Organisation definition states probiotics are 'live micro-organisms which when administered in adequate amounts confer a health benefit on the host'. From a dietary point of view, to be labelled 'probiotic' a food must contain a live, 'viable', strain of (usually lactic acid producing) bacteria with known health benefits. Research into probiotics has focused on groups of diseased subjects and positive benefits in healthy populations have been difficult to demonstrate. Studies continue to define the action of probiotics and suggest some potential benefits in the regulation of the inflammatory response in cells, protection against absorption of 'unfriendly' micro-organisms and a possible role in increasing the activity of 'natural killer cells', thereby potentially protecting against abnormal tumour cell growth. Cautionary advice may be given, however, recommending the avoidance of 'live' yoghurts if your white blood cell count is low (neutropenia). Remember, the definitive guide is best to come from a registered dietitian or your doctor. In the absence of advice to the contrary, do try a delicious fruit smoothie to start your day – (see page 53).

Movement is marvellous

Sarah Gibbings

More and more oncologists and cancer charities are recognising the benefits of exercise – and they're actively calling for it to become part of everyone's treatment.

If you have breast cancer, the World Cancer Research Fund UK recommends at least 30 minutes of moderate intensity exercise every day to improve your chance of recovery by 30 to 40 per cent. Although it may seem contradictory, this level of exercise will also help you feel less tired, as well as minimise other side-effects, such as anxiety and nausea. That doesn't mean you have to hit the gym or train for a marathon, (although some people do just that, very successfully). Moderate intensity exercise is anything that gets you breathing faster and feeling warmer, so it could be as simple as a walk in the park or climbing the stairs. Cycling, swimming and dancing are other good examples.

That 30-minute target needn't be daunting. Your body doesn't mind if you break it down into manageable chunks of a few minutes at a time. If you make the effort to move a little throughout the day, you'll not only feel better but be giving your body the best possible chance of getting better. For simple exercises to get started see page 293.

Things to think about before you start

In the first instance, talk to your specialist nurse, GP or oncologist. Bring up any concerns and ask for advice about what you can and can't do. Here are a few things to consider:

- if you have peripheral neuropathy in your feet, get properly measured for supportive shoes and check your feet before and after exercise to make sure you haven't hurt yourself (keep a close eye on your hands as well)
- wear loose, comfortable clothing and sturdy shoes, preferably trainers. Get expert advice on an appropriate sports bra, if you need one
- if you wear a wig, you may get too hot. Consider something lighter or go *au naturel*
- remember that any kind of activity is better than none – even walking to the kitchen and back during a TV ad break is worth it
- take it gently – you will make progress gradually and listen to your body. If there's any hint of sharp pain, **STOP**. Muscular tension is different and generally fine
- remember to breathe – out when you're making an effort, in when your body is relaxing before the next effort
- drink plenty of water and stay hydrated. Try adding cucumber or lemon if plain tap water doesn't taste right.

When to start

It's common sense that you'll cope better with treatment and surgery if you're as fit as you can be. As soon as you've had a diagnosis, ask your medical team what exercise they recommend, as each case is different. This section concentrates on exercise needs post-op and during treatment but the exercises on pages 295 - 305 can also help you prepare for your treatment.

The charity Breast Cancer Care recommends doing simple mobilisation exercises in the week following surgery – even the day after, if you feel up to it. This can keep you supple and retain your range of movement as your body heals. But that's only the start. You need to exercise throughout and beyond treatment, to improve your mood, keep your heart and lungs healthy and help with weight control. This is especially important, as fat produces substances including oestrogen and insulin that can promote tumour growth. Research also shows that exercise itself helps to reduce the production of some of these substances.

Breast reconstruction & exercise

In many cases, your surgeon will want you to start gentle stretching and mobilising exercises, such as shoulder rolls, in the days and weeks after surgery. It can be helpful to do these after a warm shower, when your muscles and skin will be more flexible. Walking is also recommended.

For the first couple of weeks after surgery, you should be careful with some everyday actions, such as lifting your arm above your head or behind your back. You shouldn't lift anything heavier than a bag of sugar or use the arm on the side where you've had surgery to push yourself up from the bed, open doors or pull washing out of the machine.

Your medical team will tell you when it's okay to start more formal exercise, depending on the type of reconstruction you've had and the time it takes to heal.

Central lines & ports

If you have a central line or port, you need to take a few precautions to avoid dislodging it or causing a clot or infection. The basic rules are to keep arm and chest movements slow and deliberate and to avoid heavy weights. If you have a line in your arm, don't play sports such as golf and tennis, which involve a lot of arm movement and rotation. Swimming is also off the menu, as you could get an infection. Repetitive arm movements, such as those involved in vacuuming, raking, using the arms on a cross-trainer or even some dance classes, are also on the list of things to avoid. With a port in your chest, you can swim but should avoid anything that demands strong use of your chest muscles – you may be relieved to hear that press-ups are off the agenda. Always talk to your medical team before starting an exercise programme and ask their advice.

Lymphoedema & exercise

Exercise can help to prevent or minimise lymphoedema. It gets fluid moving through the lymphatic system and can reduce swelling but you may need to favour an arm with lymphoedema. For example, if you're carrying shopping or using weights, you may need a lighter bag or weight on the affected side. Just do what you can and congratulate yourself for making even the smallest progress.

If you have a compression sleeve, check with your medical team when you should wear it. For example, you might not need it when you take a walk but should put it on before doing arm exercises. Go to page 327 for exercises specifically designed to help with arm lymphoedema.

Radiotherapy & exercise

Skin reaction to radiotherapy can make it uncomfortable to do exercises that involve your arms or chest. You may need to avoid these until this settles – but don't let that put you off walking or any other form of activity that you enjoy that doesn't cause irritation or pain. The chlorine in swimming pools can also cause irritation, so do check with your medical team before diving in.

Hormone therapy & exercise

One possible side effect of hormone therapy is joint pain. This isn't a reason not to exercise – moving can actually reduce pain, as the lubricating fluid in the joints warms up and makes each action smoother. You may find that an over-the-counter painkiller will also help. As with any medication, check with your medical team to make sure it won't react with your treatment.

Friends & family

Friends and family can do so much to help. Make a regular date to walk together, do some stretching or gentle exercises. Set targets – for example, to go up and down the stairs or to walk twice around the garden. Their encouragement and positive input can make a huge difference.

IMPORTANT – a word on exercise

Always consult your medical team before starting an exercise programme. The information in this book is not designed to replace your doctor's independent medical judgement or advice.

The exercises, instructions and advice in this book are strictly for people who have first been given medical clearance. Please be aware that not all exercises are suitable for every person and exercise is not without risks. These or any other set of exercises may result in injury.

If at any point you begin to feel pain, faintness or dizziness, you should stop immediately and consult your doctor.

For more info – please go to wellbeingexercise.co.uk

Hair, scalp, skin & nail health

Ian Carmichael MVO

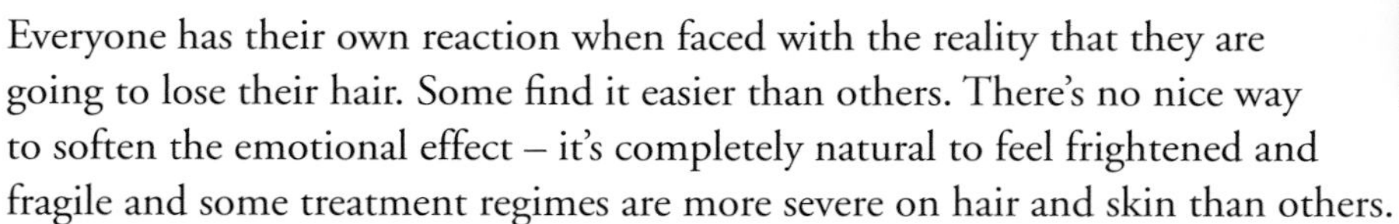

Everyone has their own reaction when faced with the reality that they are going to lose their hair. Some find it easier than others. There's no nice way to soften the emotional effect – it's completely natural to feel frightened and fragile and some treatment regimes are more severe on hair and skin than others.

The good news is an increasing number of salons and hairstylists have specialist training and experience of taking people in treatment through their journey. The availability of cold caps and scalp cooling techniques has also vastly increased in chemo suites and cancer wards and is an option offered by some cancer treatment specialists in the UK and overseas. Check if this is available for you, as it must coincide with the start of treatment and not begin during or after. When I meet someone who has just received a cancer diagnosis, the first thing we do is think about the positive and work out what professional advice and support is needed. Then we map out a plan, (which usually changes along the way, but it's a great place to start).

Planning with a qualified hair and skin care professional will help you explore the options and prepare for essential decisions.

Keeping your scalp, hands, feet & skin as healthy as possible

Good nutrition is essential for healthy hair and skin. Protein is a fundamental building block and is an important nutrient when cells renew themselves. So what you eat is as important for looking good as it is for feeling good.

Every hair follicle needs good nutrition. Essential nutrients are part of the cell renewal process and the important vitamins include biotin, pantothenic acid (vitamin B5), folate, iron, zinc and selenium. Generally, breast cancer treatment doesn't cause major problems with food tolerance and it may be that you find yourself eating more heartily than before, with the sheer joy of eating being one of those simple pleasures during your treatment.

If you're not in the mood to eat, try every way possible to encourage your appetite naturally because the nutrients you get from eating whole foods are always the best quality sources of nutrition. While it can sometimes be helpful to take a tailor-made supplement, its important to be sure the supplements you take won't interfere with your treatment. There are also topical products that are designed to be absorbed into the skin and scalp that can be helpful. If for any reason you can't manage to eat well, ask your specialist team for further advice.

Does my hairdresser have the expertise to really help?

There's no doubt that managing the changes to your hair and skin during treatment requires more expertise than basic hairdressing and skin care but there isn't a specific professional qualification.

There are standards, though, and you should expect a specially trained adviser to fully address:

- step-by-step preparation leading up to treatment information resource and expertise in appropriate topical treatments, such as shampoos and moisturisers
- style guidance including your existing hair, wigs, head coverings and new hair
- privacy in every aspect of your consultation, including a quiet secluded area for your visits, should you wish it
- an approach that's in line with published guidance as set out by the local medical authority (in the UK, the NHS and Department of Health)
- insight into current best practice and emerging treatment technology, such as cold caps
- aftercare services, where appropriate, and support networks available to you.

With chemotherapy and other treatment, hair loss is almost always temporary. If your treatment is chemo, your hair will likely return within three to six months. There are, however, other medications, (not necessarily prescribed for breast cancer treatment), that can result in hair loss or hair thinning and there are other factors that can trigger alopecia, (the partial or complete absence of hair from areas of the body where it normally grows; baldness), including the shock of diagnosis, stress, response to treatment or a hereditary predisposition.

Sometimes, when hair grows back, it's a different colour, texture or even shape. This is because the follicles are either new or changed by treatment so, as they strengthen and mature, your hair will do so as well. In older people who had natural hair colour before treatment, the new growth may be completely grey or the regrown hair will be a different colour to before. New hair is often very fine and soft and will keep changing for a while during the months after chemo has finished.

Embrace the changes! You can't control them but you can control how you react to them and, most importantly, find some expert support such as a hairdresser who has training and experience to guide you through your journey.

Is my hairdresser a wig specialist?

There are more decisions than you might first imagine when it comes to choosing a wig. In the first instance, cost is a big consideration, closely followed by your choice of natural or synthetic hair. For instance, if you are naturally grey and want to remain so, a synthetic wig is likely your only option and matching your exact hair colour and texture can be a real challenge, so an open mind is an asset. Then there's fit, comfort, maintenance, style and re-styling. It really is invaluable to have a specialist guide you through it all.

It may be that you have a special occasion coming up and you'd like a wig in an appropriate style.

Find out if there's a wig library near you. These are usually charity-based services and there might be one in your area.

What hair products are best?

Advice on hair products is essential to make your hair a lot easier to manage. The sensitivity of your scalp and skin is unpredictable and can change quickly and without warning. It can also vary depending on your treatment cycle, so be prepared for good days and bad days. I always recommend that you treat yourself on good days, usually when you are at the top of your treatment cycle, you'll associate looking good with feeling good.

Off the shelf products including shampoo, conditioner and moisturisers might contain components that your skin and scalp can become quite sensitive to such as perfume, salt and alcohol. There are also strong chemicals in hair colouring, perming and straightening solutions such as ammonia, ammonium hydroxide and thioglycosates that should be avoided during the most sensitive stages of your treatment. This applies to both store bought and salon products and it is another good reason to have a qualified stylist read the labels with you and give you guidance.

For extreme scalp irritation, have your oncologist or doctor refer you to a dermatologist. You can also ask your pharmacist about neutral products.

It isn't all doom and gloom. There are ingredients that have a positive influence on skin, scalp and hair. Here are a few to look for and ask about:

- first and foremost – the one ingredient that's so frequently overlooked is the most basic – water. Hydration is the foundation to every aspect of hair, skin and nail health
- proteins in topical treatments, such as hydrolised keratin, wheat protein and wheat amino acids – these replace the natural keratins that treatment destroys in our hair and restore strength
- plant oils, such as jojoba and almond can help hair follicles and make brittle hair more supple
- plant oils with a high concentration of vitamin E, such as wheat germ oil and sunflower oil, can help protect hair from UV damage and general dryness
- soothing ingredients, including aloe vera, chamomile, geranium, bergamot and rosemary can be found as salves as well as tinctures for deep tissue penetration and can be gentle on the scalp. Their natural fragrance can also be calming
- paraffin-based moisturisers, antimicrobials and bath emollients can be helpful for irritated and sensitive skin.

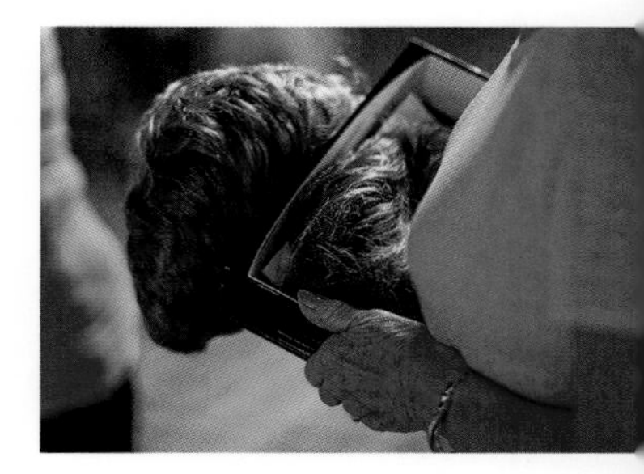

Don't leave your smile behind

When you're preparing for treatment, remember that your mouth is as sensitive as your hair and skin – perhaps even more so. The cells in your mouth are very fast growing and as such are some of the earliest to be affected. There are a few easy steps you can take to give you a bit of a head start:

- if you can, visit your dentist before you start treatment for some expert advice
- brush gently and often
- throw away that old toothbrush – it can contain bacteria best avoided during treatment
- find toothpaste, mouth wash or rinse that you like and remember that your tastebuds may change so you might need to experiment a little
- your lips don't have melanin to protect them from the UV exposure, so use neutral lip balms.

What's so brave about being bald? I've not fought for my country or found the cure for cancer – I've just gone out without my hat on! Gail Porter

Fruit cubes & yoghurt, see page 54

Smoothies & shakes

Tropical freeze

Very berry breakfast

Mint pineapple cooler

Fruit cubes & yoghurt

Spicy orange granita

Tomorange

Peanut butter & banana shake

Cool bananas

Mince pie milkshakes

Blueberry & yoghurt whippie

Here comes the sun

A wee boost to start the day

Juices, smoothies and yoghurts are a perfect way to set you up for the day, especially when your appetite might be in need of a little encouragement.
They can be a quick and easy way to have a nutritious breakfast in a glass when time is tight and they'll boost your intake of many nutrients. Check out the thumbs-up guide for each recipe.

When yoghurt is an ingredient, you'll boost your calcium, protein and B group vitamins. Probiotic yoghurts may offer some extra benefits as well.

Smoothies and shakes are simple and can be made in infinite combinations. Simply put everything into a blender and whip until smooth. Adding yoghurt makes a creamier smoothie, you can adjust the thickness using extra ice, frozen yoghurt or ice cream, all of which will adjust the nutritional content somewhat.

If you've been advised to limit or cut out dairy, bananas will also create a thicker, creamier consistency without adding fat. Also, pre-frozen fruits are readily available and convenient.

If you're sensitive to seeds, pith and skins, pass the liquidised smoothie through a sieve before serving. All of these mixtures can be frozen in ice cube trays or lolly moulds to make small treats. They can be soothing on dry and tender mouths and can help to combat plastic mouth or the metallic taste that may be a side effect of your treatment. For more about the dairy products see page 22.

Get moving

Rise and shine

Bodies are like old-fashioned engines: they need warming up before they're ready to get going, so kick-start your day with some gentle movement.

Mobilisation exercises will get your blood circulating more quickly and ease your joints. They're especially useful in the weeks and months during and after surgery or treatment, when many people curl in on themselves instinctively. That can leave you hunched and tight, cause further discomfort, affect your breathing and limit your range of motion – all of which can mean you might not be able to cope with day-to-day life as well as you'd like. You'll find some mobilisation exercise suggestions on page 295.

Looking good feels better

Here I come, ready or not!

Your style is a reflection of how you feel. It tells the world how you want to be perceived and it's a key component of your wellbeing. Skin damage and hair loss caused by cancer treatment can have an enormous effect on your confidence. This is one aspect of your new life that you do have some control over. You can turn a few of your lemons into lemonade!

A great place to start is to find out if your hairdresser has training and experience of working with people who have had cancer treatment. If not, find one. Next, think about changing your hairstyle – go short!

Your hair is likely to change anyway, so take control of it. Post-treatment hair usually returns to its original state but this takes time, so having a plan with an experienced professional can remove the fear of not knowing what to expect and the anxiety of making decisions when you're not feeling your best. Also take care of your skin, scalp and mouth.

Most importantly, don't be hard on yourself. So many people think, 'I have bigger things to worry about than my hair and appearance; I'm not supposed to feel vain'. Nonsense!

Tropical freeze

Serves 4 (very easy to prepare)

This is a really refreshing smoothie. The sorbet adds zing that helps with dry mouth and can act as an appetite stimulant.

½ fresh pineapple, skin & eyes removed*
1 mango, peeled & stone removed
1 generous scoop lemon or lime sorbet
a dash of pineapple juice
extra ice cubes for thickness

Put everything in a blender and mix until smooth (use more or less ice for desired thickness).

Each portion provides 1g protein and 90kcals.

* see *The basics & extras,* page 285

nutrient	thumbs-up score
vitamin C	👍👍👍

analysis for double portion	
vitamin C	>👍👍👍👍
fibre	👍
thiamin	👍
magnesium	<👍
vitamin B6	<👍

Very berry breakfast

Serves 2 full 250 ml portions or 4 light 120 ml portions (very easy to prepare)

What a great way to start the day! Pre-mixed frozen fruit is readily available. This smoothie is everyone of my books because it's my favourite breakfast friend. It's simply the best!

100 g yoghurt
225 g mixed apple & cranberry juice
1 slice pineapple, skin & eyes removed*
225 g fresh or frozen mixed berries
100 g strawberries

Put everything into a blender and mix until smooth. If you want a creamier smoothie use more yoghurt and if you want to adjust the thickness use ice.

Each 250 ml portion provides 4g protein and 160kcals.

* see *The basics & extras,* page 285

nutrient	thumbs-up score
vitamin C	>👍👍👍👍
vitamin B6	>👍👍👍👍
calcium	👍👍
fibre (non-starch polysaccaride)	👍👍
phosphorus	👍👍
iodine	👍👍
folate	👍👍
potassium	👍👍
magnesium	👍
iron	👍
copper	👍
thiamin	👍
riboflavin	👍
protein	👍

Mint pineapple cooler ⚖

Serves 4 (easy to prepare)

A combination that shouts 'I'm fresh!' Add a dollop of honey if you fancy it a bit sweeter.

1 small bunch of fresh mint
300 ml water
1 slice of pineapple, skin & eyes removed*
100 ml pineapple juice
6 to 8 ice cubes
sprigs of fresh mint for garnish

Pour boiling water over the mint leaves and allow to steep for 8 to 10 minutes then stir in the honey if using.

Strain the mint infusion into a blender and add the fresh pineapple and juice. Blend until smooth. At this point either add the ice cubes to make a smoothie or pour over crushed ice.

Each portion provides 1g protein and 30kcals.

* see *The basics & extras,* page 285

nutrient	thumbs-up score
vitamin C	👍

analysis for double portion	
vitamin C	👍👍
folate	👍
iron	👍

Fruit cubes & yoghurt — illustrated on page 48 ⚖

Serves 4 (easy to prepare)

This is a delicious cooler and a great source of vitamin C.

500 ml fruit juice or fruit purée
a pinch of sugar (if preparing purée)
125 g yoghurt
125 ml water

Pour the juices into ice cube trays and freeze. For the purées, place various fruits into a blender with a pinch of sugar and mix until smooth. Pass through a sieve, pour into ice cube trays and freeze.

When ready to serve, fill a glass with fruit cubes. Mix the yoghurt and water in a blender until frothy and pour over the cubes.

Each portion provides 8g protein and 210kcals.

nutrient	thumbs-up score
vitamin C	>👍👍👍👍
vitamin A	👍
vitamin B12	👍
folate	👍
thiamin	👍
calcium	👍
phosphorus	👍

Spicy orange granita ⚖

Serves 12 small portions (very easy to prepare)

This recipe is from my friend Tenzo Patricia Dravis Greene's book about Zen and food, A Feast of the Senses. *It's a palate cleanser that's so fresh, simple and delicious. As a 'Tenzo' – a chef with extensive Zen Buddhist training, Pat uses all her senses and positive energy when preparing her food. A little Zen could be a big lift when going through tough times.*

3 cups of freshly squeezed organic orange juice
1 bottle of dry sparkling wine or non-alcoholic sparkling wine
¼ tsp five-spice powder
12 mandarin oranges
12 orange segments with cuticles removed
sprigs of mint to garnish

Prepare the mandarin orange cups in advance by cleanly cutting off one third of the tops of the oranges. Scoop out the orange segments taking care not to break the skin. Store in an airtight container in the fridge until ready to use.

To make the granita, whizz the orange flesh in a blender and pass through a fine sieve. Mix this together with the orange juice, an equal amount of fizzy wine and the five-spice powder. Pour into a flat, airtight container and freeze overnight. The next morning scrape the mixture with a fork to form crystals.

To serve, fill the orange shells with the granita crystals and garnish with an orange slice and a fresh mint leaf. Serve immediately.

For a simple and quick version, spoon the granita into a silicon muffin tin, freeze and pop the single portions into a small cup to serve.

Each portion provides 2g protein and 200 kcals.

nutrient	thumbs-up score
vitamin C	>👍👍👍👍
folate	👍👍
thiamin	👍

Tomorange

Serves 4 (very easy to prepare)

'Tomorange, tomorange, I love you tomorange, you're only a day away.' That's what I always sing when I make this!

4 beefsteak tomatoes
3 oranges
a few ice cubes

nutrient	thumbs-up score
vitamin C	>👍👍👍👍
folate	👍👍
vitamin A (total retinol equivalents)	👍
vitamin B6	👍
thiamin	👍
fibre (as non-starch polysaccharide)	👍

Halve the tomatoes and oranges then squeeze using a regular citrus press juicer. Pass through a sieve. That's it. Serve on ice.

If you have an ice crusher this makes a great granita that's wonderfully soothing for a dry mouth or throat. Crushed ice by the bag is available from most supermarkets.

Each portion provides 3g protein and 80kcals.

Peanut butter & banana shake

Serves 4 (very easy to prepare)

When I was a kid peanut butter and banana sandwiches were one of my favourites. They still are, so this is for the kid in all of us!

2 ripe bananas
125 ml yoghurt, frozen yoghurt or milk
4 tbsp peanut butter
1 tbsp sugar (optional)

Cut the banana into chunks and place all ingredients in a blender and mix until thick and smooth. Add a drizzle of milk if too thick and more ice or frozen yoghurt if too thin. Easy-peasy!

Each portion provides 9g protein and 290kcals.

nutrient	thumbs-up score
vitamin B6	👍
vitamin C	👍
niacin	👍
copper	👍
magnesium	👍
phosphorus	👍

analysis for double portion	
vitamin B6	👍👍
vitamin C	👍👍
niacin	👍👍
copper	👍👍
magnesium	👍👍
phosphorus	👍👍
folate	👍
riboflavin	👍
thiamin	👍
calcium	👍
fibre (as non-starch polysaccharide)	👍
iodine	👍
potassium	👍
protein	👍
zinc	👍

Cool bananas ⚖

Serves 4 (very easy to prepare)

Anyone that's met me eventually ends up with 'cool bananas' in their vocabulary. I have no idea what it means or where it came from – it just sounds happy.

3 peaches, peeled & stone removed (1 tin)
2 bananas
a squeeze of lime juice
150 ml apple juice
100 g probiotic yoghurt drink (or yoghurt)
a few ice cubes

nutrient	thumbs-up score
vitamin C	👍👍👍👍

analysis for double portion	
vitamin C	>👍👍👍👍
vitamin B6	👍
magnesium	👍
potassium	👍
phosphorus	👍
zinc	👍

Put everything in a blender and whip up. That's it! Serve immediately.

Each portion provides 2g protein and 105kcals.

Mince pie milkshakes

Serves 6 (very easy to prepare)

'Wow, what can I say!' I was at a friend's restaurant and he served his chef's version of these. It was like drinking Christmas. If you prefer less dairy use frozen yoghurt and dairy substitutes that you are comfortable with. The flavour will be the same.

4 pre-made mince pies
750 ml vanilla ice cream, slightly softened
500 ml milk

Place the mince pies in a food processor or blender and liquidise. Next add the ice cream and whip until completely smooth. At this point you can place the mixture in the freezer and store until ready to use.

To make the shakes, add equal amounts of the mixture and milk then blend until smooth and serve immediately.

Each portion contains 9g protein and 430k cals.

nutrient	thumbs-up score
vitamin B12	4
iodine	2
riboflavin	2
vitamin A (total retinol equivalents)	1
calcium	1
phosphorus	1
protein	1
thiamin	1

Blueberry & yoghurt whippie ⚖

Serves 2 full portions

There is something serenely appealing about the colour and texture of this little number and I can't decide whether it's a breakfast or pudding! Having said that, blueberries and chocolate, mmm.

100 g frozen yoghurt
250 ml blueberries, frozen (reserve a few for garnish)
a splash of milk
1 chocolate flake per serving

Place the frozen blueberries and yoghurt in a blender and whiz until smooth. If you want a creamier drink, add a bit of milk. If you prefer a frozen parfait spoon the mixture into a glass and place back in the freezer for 20 minutes or add some ice while blending. Garnish with fresh blueberries, a sprig of mint and chocolate flake*.

* For our international friends, a '*flake*' is a small chocolate log (as pictured). In the UK, they are synonymous with summertime. A visit to the seaside wouldn't be complete without stopping at the 'Mr Softie' van for a '99' (an ice cream & flake).

Each portion provides 4g protein and 260kcals.

*see *The basics & extras,* page 285

nutrient	thumbs-up score
vitamin B6	>👍👍👍👍
vitamin B12	👍👍
vitamin C	👍👍
phosphorus	👍

Bircher muesli, see page 69

Breakfast

Off to a great start

The devil on one side & an angel on the other

In the UK, the breakfast foods we love are also some of the most controversial for people undergoing treatment. Bacon, eggs, sausage, dairy, coffee, and grapefruit – there are times when these foods hit the headlines as foods to avoid but they're also some of the most nutritious.

Not only that, during treatment there can be side-effects that change how food tastes or how comfortable it is to swallow so any ingredient that gives a real boost to flavour, offers a zing of citrus or is something smooth and soothing can be just what you need to improve nutritional intake at that time. We're not talking about pounds of processed meats, dozens of eggs, orchards of grapefruit or gallons of milk here, rather recognising that balance is important and that no one food should be labelled as 'healthy' or 'unhealthy'. It's much more about the eating pattern within which that food features.

How many times have you heard or said, 'I know breakfast is the most important meal of the day but I'm just not a breakfast person'. Well, breakfast is the most important meal of the day because it sets us up for healthy weight management and breaks the fast to provide the energy you need to get you going. Eating breakfast can also help to regulate and maintain blood glucose levels and encourage a nutritional intake to support your body's metabolism.

BUT when in treatment, it can also be the most difficult time of the day to think about eating. Sometimes there simply isn't an obvious answer.

Having a gentle morning chat about what to eat each day can have an enormous positive impact. It's one way of making food part of feeling well and returning to health, not associating it as part of your treatment. It isn't always that easy though, especially when your appetite, let alone desire to talk about meals, is at a low ebb or doesn't even exist. On the other hand, it's an opportunity to think through the vital nutrition you need to stay strong enough to fight both the cancer and manage any treatment side-effects.

As a carer, I came to rely on three things: careful listening, creativity and experimentation. If I heard the word beans, then beans it was. If I heard the word egg, I'd suggest ways of preparing them that were visually appealing and to experiment I'd suggest new foods. The latter was helpful as it gave an indication as to how my husband's taste and appetite was changing. To be honest, these are attributes that we should all embrace when in full health – it's not rocket science.

Get moving

Carers need care too

If you're part of the support team looking after someone with breast cancer, it's all too easy to put yourself last. Many carers live on heightened levels of adrenaline because they are always on alert. Whilst their energy levels remain high, their reserves often become depleted and their anxiety gets buried. This can have serious repercussions. As a carer you need to look after yourself too.

Joining in with exercise sessions or heading off for some active 'me time' is one of the best ways to do that. It'll lift your mood, boost your immune system and take your mind off things.

You can do all the exercises in this book with the person you're caring for but it's worth scheduling in 30 minutes every day for something physical that you enjoy, whether it's a bike ride, a walk, yoga, pilates or a strength session. If you can get to a regular class or the gym as well, that's even better – it'll allow you to escape from your everyday concerns and return refreshed.

It isn't selfish to prioritise your own health. You need to stay fit so you maintain the physical and mental energy you need for your loved ones.

Looking good feels better

Starting out

Beginning a treatment regime means there are going to be quite a few changes. Some of them aren't in our control and some are. Getting acquainted with various recommended hair, nail and skin treatments is an affirmative step and it may also help you plan which products to use as you go through your treatment.

Establish a routine for taking care of your hair, skin and nails. Talk to a specialist cancer nurse to start with. Then seek out a local cancer support network and ask about specialist hair and beauty advice for people going through treatment.

There are people with broad experience out there that may know of others who have coped with similar hair and skin care issues. Specialist cancer nurses also have experience of relief products – both tried and true and what's new.

Waffles

Serves 4 (easy to prepare)

These waffles are light, fluffy and crunchy in one. They're best right off the griddle but reheat well. This is breakfast that craves good company.

160 g flour
4 tsp baking powder
½ tsp salt
2 tsp sugar
100 g butter, melted
400 ml milk
2 eggs, separated
2 to 3 extra knobs of butter for cooking

your choice of toppings for serving

butter & maple syrup
crème fraîche & blackberries
strawberries & cream
Nutella & bananas

You will need a waffle iron to prepare this dish.

In a dry, clean bowl, sift together the dry ingredients, beat in the egg yolks then whisk in the milk and melted butter. Next beat the egg whites until fairly stiff and fold them into the batter.

Warm a waffle iron to medium heat and brush with butter then spoon on the mixture. Cook until lightly golden then flip and cook the same on the other side.

Keep the waffles warm and serve with favourite toppings.

Each portion provides 5g protein and 480kcals.

(3 strawberries and 25 ml double cream used for analysis)

nutrient	thumbs-up score
vitamin A (total retinol equivalents)	👍👍👍👍
vitamin B12	👍👍👍👍
phosphorus	👍👍👍👍
vitamin C	👍👍👍
sodium	👍👍👍
riboflavin	👍
iodine	👍
calcium	👍
chloride	👍

Bircher muesli – illustrated on page 64

Serves 4 (easy to prepare)

I don't think a healthy cookery book featuring breakfast would be complete without a recipe for muesli. Making it yourself means you can control the amount of sugar and swap ingredients to suit your taste. Anything goes!

100 g rolled oats (gluten-free if desired)
100 g desiccated coconut flakes
100 g dried apple, chopped
100 g pumpkin seeds (add sunflower seeds if desired)
3 tbsp coconut oil, melted
3 tbsp runny honey
2 tsp cinnamon
1 tsp vanilla extract
100 g almond flakes, toasted
50 g dehydrated berries & other fruit (such as goji, cranberries, dates or apricot)
40 g sultanas
fresh fruit & yoghurt to serve

Preheat the oven to 170ºCf. Mix the oats, coconut flakes and seeds together with the cinnamon, vanilla, coconut oil and honey. Spread evenly on a roasting tray and roast for 20 minutes until golden, stir every few minutes. Allow to cool, then mix with the remaining the ingredients and store in an airtight container.

Serve with your choice of yoghurt, milk and fresh fruit like figs, plums or berries.

Each portion provides 17g protein and 780kcals.

nutrient	thumbs-up score
copper	👍👍👍👍
phosphorus	👍👍👍👍
magnesium	👍👍👍
irom	👍👍
fibre (as non-starch polysaccharide)	👍
riboflavin	👍
thiamin	👍
protein	👍
potassium	👍
calcium	👍
zinc	👍

Breakfast bites

I can't remember when I fell in love with Rice Krispies treats – maybe the Sound of Music *was released the same year. Timeless classics never stop giving us inspiration. As an idea for little energy-filled bites, I applied the same recipe to my Bircher muesli cereal.*

Rice Krispie treats – original recipe*

Yield: 12 large squares (very easy to prepare)

nutrient	thumbs-up score
iron	👍
thiamin	👍
riboflavin	👍
niacin	👍
vitamin B6	👍
vitamin B12	👍
folate	👍

3 tbsp butter
200 g (4 cups) miniature marshmallows
150 g (6 cups) Rice Krispies cereal

Grease or line a 21 cm x 30 cm cake tin with parchment. Then, in large saucepan melt the butter over low heat. Add the marshmallows and stir until completely melted, remove from the heat and stir in the Rice Krispies until well coated. Using a spoon, press the mixture into the tin. When cool, cut into squares and store in an airtight container (if they last that long).

Each portion (two squares) provides 3g protein and 280kcals.

Bircher bites

Yield: 24 small squares (easy to prepare)

nutrient	thumbs-up score
copper	👍👍👍
phosphorus	👍👍
magnesium	👍👍
irom	👍👍
fibre (as non-starch polysaccharide)	👍👍
riboflavin	👍
thiamin	👍
niacin	👍
protein	👍
potassium	👍
calcium	👍
zinc	👍

2 tbsp butter
750 g (6 cups) bircher muesli (see page 69)
150 g (3 cups) mini-marshmallows

The method is the same as for Rice Krispie treats. The muesli is dense and will absorb more moisture and you want the bites crunchy so work quickly.

If you want the bircher bites to be even smaller, simply drop spoonful clusters onto parchment and let cool.

Note: the photograph shows some of the squares dipped in chocolate. For this you can simply melt good quality chocolate in a double boiler over hot water or microwave, dip the tops and allow to set.

Each portion (4 small squares) provides 13g protein and 700kcals.

* *The recipe for Rice Krispie treats is the original from Kellogg's. History has proven it simply can't be improved.*

Bacon & egger

Serves 1 (easy to prepare)

This breakfast to go is loved the world over and there is nothing better than to be your own drive-thru, exclude the bacon or replace with tomatoes if you prefer. For you bakers there's a sure fire English muffin recipe in The basics & extras, page 285.

1 English muffin*, halved & toasted
1 fresh, free-range egg
1 slice Cheddar cheese
1 piece back bacon, fat removed
a small knob of butter
salt & pepper

Fry the bacon in a small pan. Poach the egg* or as an alternative, beat the egg enough to break and mix the yolk with the white, add a bit of seasoning, pour into a plastic cup and pop into a microwave for 1 minute or until cooked through.

Toast and butter the muffin then build your sandwich. As a final touch, pop the sandwich back into the microwave for 10 seconds to gently melt the cheese. Wrap it in some parchment and away you go, day started!

Each portion provides 32g protein and 560kcals.

* see *The basics & extras,* page 285

nutrient	thumbs-up score
vitamin B12	>👍👍👍👍
sodium	👍👍👍👍
chloride	👍👍👍👍
calcium	👍👍👍
phosphorus	👍👍👍
vitamin A (total retinol equivalents)	👍👍
vitamin B6	👍👍
riboflavin	👍👍
thiamin	👍👍
protein	👍👍
folate	👍
niacin	👍
iodine	👍
iron	👍
selenium	👍
zinc	👍

Panna cotta with berry coulis

Serves 6 (easy to prepare)

Panna cotta for breakfast? Why not! It's easy on the tummy and even in small portions delivers good nutrition to start the day.

3 gelatin leaves
250 ml milk
250 ml double cream
100 g sugar
1 tsp vanilla extract

For the berry coulis

125 g fresh mixed berries
(save a few for garnishing)
1 tsp sugar
3 tbsp water

For the panna cotta, soak the gelatine leaves in cold water until soft. Combine the milk, cream, sugar and vanilla in a heavy bottomed pan and warm to just simmering. Remove excess water from the gelatine and stir into the cream until completely dissolved. While keeping the mixture warm, stir gently with a wooden spoon frequently enough to keep it from thickening on the sides for about 1 hour. When ready, strain through a fine sieve and pour into glasses. Refrigerate until set.

For the coulis, purée the berries, sugar and water in a blender. Pass through a fine sieve and set in the fridge until ready to use.

When ready to serve, cover the panna cotta with a thin layer of coulis, crush on a few fresh berries and if you like, decorate with edible flowers such as fuchsias, forget-me-nots or nasturtium.

Each portion provides 4g protein and 310kcals

nutrient	thumbs-up score
vitamin A (total retinol equivalents)	👍👍
vitamin B12	👍👍
vitamin C	👍
iodine	👍

This photo is taken with fuchsia, whose flowers and berries are edible

Easy eggs Arlington

Serves 4 (easy to prepare)

The Hollandaise sauce makes this dish a bit fiddly so use store bought to make it easier. It's delicious!

6 fresh eggs
50 ml milk
300 g wild smoked salmon
Hollandaise sauce*
a small jar lumpfish caviar (optional)
4 English muffins*
a knob of butter
salt & pepper

Prepare the Hollandaise in advance and keep warm for serving.

Whisk the eggs, milk and a bit of salt and pepper in a bowl then scramble in a lightly buttered pan until just cooked through. Toast and butter the English muffins.

Place the muffins on a plate then make a nest on top using the salmon strips. Spoon the eggs into the nest, drizzle with Hollandaise and top with a dollop of caviar. Serve hot.

Each serving provides 41g protein and 1240kcals.

* see *The basics & extras,* page 285

nutrient	thumbs-up score
vitamin A (total retinol equivalents)	>👍👍👍👍
vitamin B12	>👍👍👍👍
sodium	>👍👍👍👍
chloride	>👍👍👍👍
phosphorus	👍👍👍👍
protein	👍👍👍
vitamin D	👍👍
niacin	👍👍
riboflavin	👍👍
iodine	👍👍
selenium	👍👍
vitamin B6	👍
thiamin	👍
folate	👍
calcium	👍
copper	👍
iron	👍
magnesium	👍
zinc	👍

Breakfast cupcakes ⚖

Serves 6, 2 cupcakes per person (easy to prepare)

These little bundles of happiness are a super fast way to prepare a light and nutritious meal and a great way to use leftovers.

8 large, free-range eggs
4 bacon rashers, fried
100 g Emmenthal cheese, or
  Cheddar, finely grated
300 ml sour cream
300 ml milk
1 tsp mixed herbs
salt & pepper
a knob of butter

Preheat oven to 160°Cf. For this dish I use silicon cupcake moulds

Crack eggs into a bowl and beat in sour cream, milk and herbs until smooth. Be careful not to add too much air. Season to taste.

Lightly butter the moulds, sprinkle in a layer of bacon bits and cheese then pour in the egg mixture to ¾ full. Allow to bake until fully cooked, about 15 to 20 minutes. When finished they should be well risen and springy but not turning colour. Serve immediately.

Each portion provides 10g protein and 270kcals.

nutrient	thumbs-up score
vitamin B12	👍👍👍
vitamin A (total retinol equivalents)	👍👍
calcium	👍👍
phosphorus	👍👍
sodium	👍👍
chloride	👍👍
riboflavin	👍
copper	👍
protein	👍

Old-fashioned French toast ⚖

Serves 4 (very easy to prepare)

Though not a nutritional giant French toast is comfort food at its best and is a great part of a full breakfast. Add your favourite fresh berries for added nutrition and flavour.

8 slices day old white bread
4 eggs
250 ml milk
½ tsp cinnamon
a knob of butter
maple syrup to serve

Mix eggs, milk and cinnamon in a shallow dish.

Melt a knob of butter in a medium hot pan taking care not to burn. Next dip a bread slice on both sides in egg mixture so it is wet but not soggy. Fry in the pan to golden on both sides then remove and keep warm. Repeat with the rest of the slices.

Serve with maple syrup and a dollop of butter.

Each portion provides 5g protein and 210kcals.

nutrient	thumbs-up score
sodium	👍
chloride	👍
selenium	👍

Cheese soufflé ⚖

Serves 4 as a starter for breakfast, 2 as a main

Soufflés are such a luxurious way to serve eggs, which are often one of the few foods that one can tolerate when undergoing treatment.

(You will need 1-15 cm soufflé dish or 4 ramekins)
melted butter to grease the dishes
fine white bread crumbs
40 g butter
30 g plain flour
½ tsp English mustard powder
a dash of sriracha*
300 ml milk, warmed
80 g cheese, grated (Gruyere, Parmesan, Roquefort or Cheddar)
4 large eggs, separated
salt & pepper

Preheat oven to 200°Cf and place a baking tray higher than centre. Make sure your dish or ramekins are very clean and dry, then brush with melted butter and very lightly dust with bread crumbs.

Next, in a heavy saucepan, melt the butter on low heat, stir in the flour then add the mustard and sriracha and let cook for just one minute. (If using Roquefort or blue cheese forgo the mustard). Gradually add the milk until the mixture is smooth and comes to the boil. Stir constantly. Allow to boil for 2 minutes. The mixture should get quite thick and leave the sides of the pan.

Remove from the heat and stir in the cheese and egg yolks. Season to taste. It should be thick but able to pour.

In a separate, clean and dry bowl, whisk the egg whites until just stiff then add a spoonful to the cheese mixture. Gently fold in the remainder and pour into the soufflé dish or ramekins to ¾ full.

Bake for approximately 20 to 30 minutes for the large dish and 8 to 10 minutes for the ramekins. Do not open the oven door until ¾ through the baking time. To check for readiness give the dish a little push. If the soufflé wobbles, cook for about 5 minutes more for large and 1 for small.

Serve immediately.

Each portion provides 9g protein and 260kcals.

* see *The basics & extras,* page 285

nutrient	thumbs-up score
vitamin B12	👍👍👍
potassium	👍
vitamin A (total retinol equivalents)	👍
iodine	👍
phosphorus	👍
sodium	👍
chloride	👍

(our analysis has been done as 4 individual ramekins)

Porridge & cinder toffee

Serves 4 (medium difficulty to prepare)

Oatmeal is a great way to start your day. Even in small portions. It is easy to digest, releases energy slowly and packed with essential goodness.

For the cinder toffee

200 g caster sugar
4 tbsp golden syrup
1 tbsp bicarbonate of soda

For the porridge

650 ml water
350 ml milk
100 g oats, rolled or steel-cut

To make the cinder toffee, generously grease a clean and dry 22 cm metal cake tin or line an aluminium tray with a silpat mat.

In a deep, heavy pan add the sugar and syrup on medium-low heat and allow the sugar to melt. Do not stir. This will take 3 to 4 minutes. The mixture should be fully melted and bubbling but don't let it turn brown.

Remove from heat and add the soda. The mixture will fizz, foam and rapidly expand. Stir lightly to ensure all the soda is evenly mixed. Immediately pour into the cake tin and set aside to cool until cool-hardened. When set chop into desired bits or use a rolling pin to grind into chunky sprinkles.

To prepare the porridge, follow the manufacturer's instructions. I suggest that instead of boiling the oats in water only, you use a 1 to 3 mixture of water and milk. This is a way of getting a bit of extra calcium and nutrition in. It can also make the porridge stodgier so watch your cooking time.

Serve hot and sprinkle with cinder toffee and drizzle with a bit of honey. Add a few berries for colour and texture.

Each portion provides 3g protein and 340kcals.

nutrient	thumbs-up score
fibre (as non-starch polysaccharide)	👍👍👍
vitamin B12	👍👍
sodium	👍👍
chloride	👍
vitamin C	👍
iodine	👍

Prawn avocado cocktail, see page 92

Light bites

Beetroot hummus & pitta toasties

Marinated pepper & goats' cheese crostini

Italian stuffed bread

Prawn avocado cocktail

Smoked trout with horseradish mousse

Shiitake sushi

Perfect pretzels

Tapas tortilla

Bruschetta with broad bean pesto

Asparagus with courgette ribbons

BBQ salsa, guacamole & tortilla chips

Goats' cheese & chestnut tart

Mushroom duxelle on melba toast

Spanakopita & tzatziki

Cheese grisini

Elevensies

Little & often

Little and often. It's a perky little statement that gets the point across but for any chemo suite warrior it's a fine line. Food is one of the few things that remains familiar and it's something we can be in charge of when undergoing treatment.

We all have to eat and drink. Listen to your body and encourage your brain when it comes to meals. A slow gentle start is good for everyone.

A cancer diagnosis can have any number of effects on how, what, when, where and why we eat but one thing is undeniable, providing your body with the nutrition it needs to tackle the disease and recover from treatment is really important. Go for the most nutritious foods you can when your appetite is small or your food tolerance is variable as it's not just any old calories you need.

Concentrate on the positives. Try to savour the smell of freshly baked bread, the sound of bacon sizzling in the pan, the sight of a dramatic brandy flambé, the creamy texture of a soufflé just out of the oven. Tasting is just part of the experience. Don't forget to enjoy it with the rest of your senses as well.

There's something irresistible about in between time light dishes. It's the perfect solution to using odd bits and leftovers as well. Here are a few sumptuous light dishes that are generally easy to prepare and a delight anytime.

Get moving

A walk in the park

Simply being outside can lift the spirits and going for a walk can give you an even bigger boost because you're taking in extra oxygen. Add a friend or two and it'll become a social occasion.

To improve your heart, lungs and muscles (and burn more calories), swing or pump your arms as you go and vary your pace. For example, walk slowly between two lampposts or bushes, then faster between the next two, then at a middling pace, then slowly again. Lengths of your garden or the street will do the job just as well.

Throwing a ball or stick for a dog will improve your range of movement – or play catch with a friend to boost your co-ordination, (and have a laugh).

Gardening has a similar effect – being surrounded by greenery has been shown to improve mood and make exercise feel easier and more rewarding. Again, alternate gentle activities, such as dead-heading, with something a bit more vigorous, such as squatting down to do some planting and getting up again, which will challenge your legs, bottom and balance. If you'd like to know more and find some other options, turn to page 302.

Looking good feeling better

The scents of it all

When other senses are challenged, your sense of smell can both change and intensify, so fragrance and odour can have an enormous impact on how you feel. Choose products that aren't perfumed or that you like the smell of.

If you can, exfoliation is helpful to remove dead cells and keep your skin and scalp feeling fresh. Serums designed to penetrate are a good method of protecting deeper layers of skin.

In addition, there are a number of clinically proven antibacterial lotions and shower and bath emulsions that can help prevent infection and soothe tender skin. Ask your pharmacist for more information.

Beetroot hummus & pitta toasties

Serves 6, approx 675g (easy to prepare)

If you like hummus, you'll love this. It's a great little number to brighten any table and it's delicious.

For the hummus

3 medium-sized beetroot, washed & trimmed
424 g (1 tin) chickpeas, drained & rinsed
50 g tahini
6 tbsp olive oil, plus a little extra
juice of 1 lemon
3 garlic cloves, puréed
2 generous tsp ground cumin (or to taste)
a dash of sriracha*
salt & white pepper to taste
a pinch of ground sumac

For the pitta toasties

6 to 8 rounds pitta bread
175 g butter
2 tbsp parsley, finely chopped
1 tbsp chives, finely chopped
1 clove garlic, puréed
1 tsp lemon juice
salt & pepper

Preheat oven to 170°Cf. Rub the beetroot with a little olive oil, place in a roasting tin and sprinkle with a bit of salt. Roast for about 40 minutes until fork tender. Allow to cool, peel the skins and chop.

Place all the ingredients in a food processor and mix until smooth and creamy. If the mixture is thick add a few drops of water. Adjust the seasoning to taste. Garnish with a sprinkle of sumac and serve with pitta toasties.

For the pitta toasties, mix all the ingredients with the butter, then spread it on the on the pittas and warm in the pre-heated oven until lightly toasted.

Each portion provides 16g protein and 690kcals.

* see *The basics & extras,* page 285

nutrient	thumbs-up score
vitamin A (total retinol equivalents)	👍👍
sodium	👍👍
chloride	👍👍
phosphorus	👍👍
fibre (non-starch polysaccharide)	👍👍
iron	👍👍
vitamin C	👍
folate	👍
thiamin	👍
calcium	👍
copper	👍
magnesium	👍
protein	👍
potassium	👍
zinc	👍

Marinated pepper & goats' cheese crostini

Yields approximately 30 pieces (easy to prepare)

The power of the pepper! These are great little morsels that burst with flavour. The marinated peppers will last for a couple weeks if refrigerated in a sealed container.

3 bell peppers
olive oil
garlic, crushed
fresh herbs, finely chopped
baguette, sliced & toasted
soft goats' cheese

Coat the peppers lightly with olive oil and grill until the skin is charred and blistered. Put in a plastic bag and leave to sweat. When cool, peel and soak in olive oil infused with garlic and a few herbs. To serve, slice finely and pile on a toasted baguette spread with soft goats' cheese.

Each portion provides 12g protein and 290kcals.

nutrient	thumbs-up score
sodium	>👍👍👍👍
chloride	>👍👍👍👍
folate	👍👍👍👍
vitamin B6	👍👍👍
vitamin B12	👍👍👍
protein	👍👍👍
vitamin A (total retinol equivalents)	👍👍
calcium	👍👍
copper	👍👍
iron	👍👍
vitamin C	👍
riboflavin	👍
thiamin	👍
fibre (as non-starch polysaccharide)	👍
magnesium	👍
zinc	👍

Italian stuffed bread

1 loaf serves 4 as a starter or snack (easy to prepare)

This is one of your best friends for so many reasons. Tomatoes and mushrooms for a start. It's filled with good nutrition and crammed with flavour. It's so fast and simple.

pre-made croissant dough or puff pastry*
a splash of olive oil
8 to 10 fine slices Parma ham
8 to 10 fine slices mozzarella cheese
2 large tomatoes, finely sliced
6 to 8 white mushrooms, finely sliced
dried Italian herbs
salt & pepper
1 egg, whisked

Preheat the oven to 170°Cf. On a floured surface, roll out the dough into a rectangle the thickness of fine piecrust. Brush with a thin film of olive oil. Layer the ham, cheese, tomatoes and mushrooms. Sprinkle generously with herbs. Roll up and tuck the ends under, brush all over with egg wash and bake for about 20 minutes until golden brown. Allow to set for about 5 minutes. Slice and serve warm.

Each portion provides 35g protein and 740kcals.

**There are two easy ways to prepare the dough. I prefer the croissant dough but puff pastry works as well. The pre-made croissant dough usually comes in a tube and is perforated into triangles. Remove the dough and make a large rectangle of dough by squidging together perforated edges. It does work.*

nutrient	thumbs-up score
sodium	>👍👍👍👍
chloride	>👍👍👍👍
folate	👍👍👍👍
vitamin B6	👍👍👍
vitamin B12	👍👍👍
protein	👍👍👍
vitamin A (total retinol equivalents)	👍👍
calcium	👍👍
copper	👍👍
iron	👍👍
phosphorus	👍👍
vitamin C	👍
riboflavin	👍
thiamin	👍
fibre (as non-starch polysaccharide)	👍
magnesium	👍
zinc	👍

Prawn avocado cocktail – illustrated on page 82

Serves 4 (easy to prepare)

It's hard to resist this all-time classic. If your tastebuds are tired you can add an extra kick to the sauce.

250 ml prawns, peeled, deveined & cooked
2 ripe avocados
iceburg lettuce, very finely shredded
freshly cracked black pepper

For the Marie Rose sauce

4 tbsp mayonnaise
2 tsp ketchup
1 tsp horseradish, finely grated
juice & zest of 1 lime
a dash of tabasco
a dash of Worcestershire sauce
20 ml vodka (the optional extra kick)

To make the sauce stir all ingredients excluding the prawns, avocado and lettuce in a bowl. Add the prawns and coat with the sauce. Place in the fridge until ready to serve.

Halve the avocados and remove the stone and peel. Dice into bite-sized chunks. To serve arrange the avocado and prawns on a small bed of shredded lettuce. Add a good turn of fresh black pepper.

Each portion provides 16g protein and 430kcals.

nutrient	thumbs-up score
vitamin B12	>👍👍👍👍
sodium	👍👍👍
chloride	👍👍👍
vitamin C	👍👍
vitamin B6	👍
riboflavin	👍
copper	👍
iodine	👍
phosphorus	👍
protein	👍
selenium	👍

Smoked trout with horseradish mousse

Serves 6 to 8 as a canapé (easy to prepare)

This is a perfect snack or fish course for a celebration meal. Smoked salmon is a great alternative.

125 g smoked trout, skin & bones removed
125 g cream cheese
2 to 3 heaped tsp fresh creamed horseradish
zest & juice of 1 lemon
a small bunch of fresh chives, finely snipped
sea salt & ground black pepper
a dash of good quality oil (to your taste)

nutrient	thumbs-up score
vitamin B12	>👍👍👍👍
sodium	👍

Put the cream cheese into a mixing bowl with the horseradish, lemon zest, half the juice and mix together. Stir in a handful of chopped chives and season to taste. You want the flavour to be a strong combination of hot, smoke and salt balanced with a bit of sweet and sour. Adjust the flavour with more horseradish or lemon juice. Flake in the trout, being careful that all skin and bones are removed then using a spatula, gently fold the mixture together so its pleasingly chunky. Spoon single servings into dishes or larger servings into ramekins, cover with cling film and chill until ready to serve.

Each portion provides 5g protein and 115kcals.

Shiitake sushi

Serves 4 as a snack (medium difficulty to prepare)

These little tidbits are easier to make than you might think.

For the mushroom filling

1 tbsp sesame oil
1 garlic clove, puréed
4 large shiitake caps, sliced into strips
2 large spring onions, greens only, sliced lengthwise
¼ cup water
1 tbsp tamari soy
a dash of sriracha*

For finishing

2 nori sheets
sesame seeds
soy sauce
wasabi
pickled ginger

For the rice

120 g sushi rice
210 ml water
a generous tsp of salt
1 tbsp rice vinegar

nutrient	thumbs-up score
vitamin B12	👍👍
sodium	👍👍
chloride	👍👍
iodine	👍

To make the rice, put the rice in a strainer and rinse under cold, running water for 1-2 minutes. Place in a small saucepan with the water, salt and rice vinegar, stir and bring to a simmer for 20 minutes until all liquid is absorbed. Remove from heat and let stand for 10 minutes, covered.

To prepare the mushroom filling, coat the bottom of a heavy-bottomed skillet with sesame oil and place over medium heat. Sauté the garlic for 1 minute then add the mushroom caps and cook for 5 minutes until lightly browned, turn over and brown the other sides until the caps are tender but still hold their shape then add the water, soy sauce and chili paste. Raise the heat to medium-high and simmer for 2 minutes until most of the liquid has evaporated. While the mushrooms are resting add the onion strips to let them lightly infuse and soften.

To roll the sushi, make sure you have a bowl of water nearby and place a nori sheet onto a bamboo rolling mat. The sheet should be no larger than the mat. Using wet hands, cover the nori with a thin layer of rice and arrange half of the mushrooms in a single line along the width of nori, about one inch away from you. Take the bamboo mat and end of nori closest to you and tightly roll it over the mushrooms. Tuck the end of the nori in and continue rolling, using the mat to press the roll tight. Once completely rolled, slice into eight pieces. Repeat using the other nori sheet and remaining rice and mushrooms.

Sprinkle with sesame seeds and serve with soy sauce, wasabi and pickled ginger.

Each portion provides 5g protein and 190kcals.

* see *The basics & extras,* page 285

Perfect pretzels ⚖

Yields 8 large pretzels (medium difficulty to prepare)

These are plain old-fashioned fun. Serve them with salt, herbs, cheese, bacon or crispy onions. The plain ones are perfect with lashings of mustard. Yum!

For the dough

2½ cups plain flour

1 tsp salt

1 tsp sugar

2¼ tsp instant yeast

1 cup warm water

For the topping

1 cup boiling water

2 tbsp baking soda

coarse salt (pepper, herbs, bacon & cheese – whatever you like!)

3 tbsp unsalted butter, melted

Make the dough by hand or using a bread machine.

By hand, place the ingredients in a bowl and combine thoroughly. Knead for 5 minutes until soft, smooth but quite slack. Flour the dough and place it in a plastic bag. Allow it to rest for 30 minutes.

By machine, place the dough ingredients into the pan and set the programme to dough or manual. Put it through the kneading cycle, cancel the programme, remove the dough then flour and place in a plastic bag to prove as above.

Next combine boiling water and baking soda, stirring until dissolved and set aside to cool to lukewarm in a 22 cm pan.

Preheat oven to 200°Cf and line a baking sheet with parchment.

Transfer the dough to a lightly greased work surface and divide it into eight pieces allow to rest uncovered for 5 minutes.

Roll each piece of dough into a 30 inch thin rope and twist into a pretzel knot or shape of your choice. Place 4 pretzels into the pan of soda water and ladle so each is completely covered. Leave them in the water for 2 minutes then transfer to the baking sheet. Sprinkle them lightly with coarse salt or preferred toppings and allow them to rest, uncovered, for 10 minutes.

Bake the pretzels for 8 to 9 minutes, or until golden brown. Remove from the oven and brush generously with melted butter. Using all the butter will give them their unctuous flavour.

Each portion provides 4g protein and 190kcals.

nutrient	thumbs-up score
sodium	👍👍
chloride	👍
folate	👍

Tapas tortilla

Serves 4 (medium difficulty to prepare)

A traditional Spanish tapas, this can be served as a tart or canapés. It stores well and a little goes a long way. Frozen broad beans (fava) are just fine to use.

20 ml olive oil
2 large Spanish white onions, thinly sliced
300 g waxy potatoes, peeled & diced
250 g broad beans
1 tsp thyme, finely chopped
6 eggs
45 g chives & flat parsley, finely chopped
salt & pepper

Heat half the oil in a deep pan. Add the onions and potatoes tossing to lightly coat. Sauté on low heat for about 30 minutes or until the potatoes are tender. Stir occasionally to prevent the onions from burning.

Meanwhile, cook the beans in a pan of salted boiling water for about 4 to 5 minutes (half the time if using frozen), drain and set aside to cool. When cool, peel and discard the outer skins. Add the beans and thyme to the potatoes and season to taste. Cook for 2 to 3 minutes until heated through.

In a separate bowl beat the eggs and herbs together with a bit of seasoning then pour the mixture over the potatoes. Increase the heat to medium and cook gently for a few minutes until the bottom is set. While cooking pull the sides of the tortilla away from the pan allowing uncooked liquid to run underneath. It will be ready when the egg is still quite soft but there is no liquid.

Now for the tricky bit, cover the frying pan with a large plate and flip the tortilla onto the plate. Add the remaining oil to the pan. When hot, slide the tortilla back into the pan and cook for another 4 to 5 minutes until the bottom is lightly golden.

Slide the tortilla back onto the plate and allow to cool. Cut into wedges or bite-sized cubes. Serve warm or cold. For a more substantial dish add a handful of diced ham to the bean mixture.

Each portion provides 25g protein and 410kcals.

nutrient	thumbs-up score
vitamin B12	>👍👍👍👍
phosphorus	👍👍👍👍
copper	👍👍👍
vitamin C	👍👍
thiamin	👍👍
fibre (as non-starch polysaccharide)	👍👍
iron	👍👍
protein	👍👍
zinc	👍👍
vitamin A (total retinol equivalents)	👍
vitamin B6	👍
riboflavin	👍
folate	👍
calcium	👍
sodium	👍
chloride	👍
iodine	👍
magnesium	👍
potassium	👍

Bruschetta with broad bean pesto

Serves 4 (medium difficulty to prepare)

For a heartier meal substitute the toast with pasta.

For the pesto

200 g broad beans
15 g basil leaves
1 large clove garlic, crushed
15 g Parmesan cheese, grated, plus extra to serve
100 ml olive oil
salt & pepper

For the bruschetta

1 baguette, sliced
1 garlic clove
1 shallot, sliced into rings
2 to 3 Italian tomatoes
fresh basil or oregano leaves, finely chopped
juice & zest of 1 lemon (to taste)
sunflower oil for frying

To prepare the pesto, cook the broad beans in boiling water for about 5 minutes, (half the time if using frozen). Drain and rinse under cold water. Shell and discard the skins. Next put the beans, basil, garlic and Parmesan cheese into a food processor and whiz for a few seconds until combined but not completely smooth. Then, with the motor running, add the oil in a steady stream until you have a thick sauce. Season to taste.

To prepare the crispy shallot, heat enough oil in pan to deep-fry the shallot rings. Heat the oil to 180°C, then place the rings into the hot oil and fry until golden then remove with a slotted spoon and drain.

Next chop the tomatoes into 4 'petals' by slicing lengthwise. Scoop out the seeds and chop roughly. Lightly mix with a drop of lemon juice, a drizzle of olive oil and salt & pepper.

To make the bruschetta, slice the baguette then lightly drizzle both sides of each slice with olive oil and season to taste. Place under a grill until just golden, flip and toast the other side. Next, cut the garlic clove in half and rub one side of the toast with it. Cover half the toast slices with the tomatoes and finish by topping with a few crispy shallot rings and sprinkle with herbs. Spread the pesto over the rest of the toasts and garnish with a pinch of lemon zest.

Each portion (two slices) provides 6g protein and 290kcals.

nutrient	thumbs-up score
vitamin B12	>👍👍👍👍
phosphorus	👍👍👍👍
copper	👍👍👍
vitamin C	👍👍
thiamin	👍👍
fibre (as non-starch polysaccharide)	👍👍
iron	👍👍
protein	👍👍
zinc	👍👍
vitamin A (total retinol equivalents)	👍
vitamin B6	👍
riboflavin	👍
folate	👍
sodium	👍
chloride	👍
calcium	👍
iodine	👍
magnesium	👍
potassium	👍

Asparagus with courgette ribbons

Serves 4, 2 parcels per person (easy to prepare)

Simplicity wins! Easy, fresh and light for any time of day.

12 spears large asparagus
1 large courgette
1 ripe cantaloupe melon

Break the asparagus ends off and trim so you are left with the tender green spears and tops. Lightly steam until cooked through yet still firm. Allow to drain on a sheet of kitchen roll.

Using the vegetable peeler, gently scrape the full length of the courgette to create long, thin ribbons. Lay flat on a sheet of kitchen roll and lightly salt to extract excess water. Leave to stand for a few minutes, turn them over and repeat on the other side.

Wrap two or three asparagus spears together in a ribbon of courgette and serve with sliced melon.

Easy!

Each portion provides 3g protein and 25kcals.

nutrient	thumbs-up score
vitamin C	>👍👍👍👍
folate	👍👍👍
vitamin A (total retinol equivalents)	👍👍
vitamin B6	👍
thiamin	👍
sodium	👍
chloride	👍
fibre (as non-starch polysaccharide)	👍
potassium	👍

BBQ salsa, guacamole & tortilla chips

Yields approximately 2 cups of each, a snack for 4 to 6 people (easy to prepare)

This is great grazing food and an easy way to digest vegetables. Add more lime to the guacamole for a stronger flavour. A small amount delivers a lot of vitamins and minerals.

For the salsa

olive oil
2 large onions, peeled
1 aubergine, thickly sliced
2 courgette, thickly sliced
3 jalapeno peppers
3 bell peppers
4 large Italian tomatoes
1 whole bulb garlic
a small bunch coriander, chopped
salt & pepper

Preheat a bbq grill until very hot, around 400°Cf. Coat the vegetables and garlic with olive oil then grill until lightly charred. Start with the onions as they take the longest. Leave the tomatoes until last. Remove from the grill.

When the peppers are well charred on the outside, sweat them in a sealed container or plastic bag. When cool enough to handle, remove the skins and seeds.

Squeeze the garlic flesh out of the husks and place in a food processor with the grilled vegetables. Blend gently until mixed but not puréed. Add coriander and season to taste. Serve with tortilla chips.

For the guacamole

3 ripe medium-size avocados, peeled & stoned
1 large Italian tomato, chopped & seeds removed
juice of 1 lime
a small bunch coriander, chopped
¼ cup crème fraîche
salt & pepper

Place the avocado meat in a bowl and coarsely mash. Fold in the remaining ingredients. If preparing in advance, store in an airtight container. Serve with tortilla chips.

For tortilla chips

Preheat oven to grill.

Cut soft flour tortillas into bite-sized triangles, place on a baking sheet and grill until just turning golden.

Each portion provides 12g protein and 595kcals.

nutrient	thumbs-up score
vitamin B6	>👍👍👍👍
vitamin C	>👍👍👍👍
vitamin A (total retinol equivalents	👍👍👍👍
fibre (as a non-starch polysaccaride)	👍👍👍
folate	👍👍👍
thiamin	👍👍
phosphorus	👍👍
potassium	👍👍
sodium	👍👍
chloride	👍👍
niacin	👍
riboflavin	👍
calcium	👍
copper	👍
iron	👍
magnesium	👍
protein	👍

Goats' cheese & chestnut tart

Yield 1 tart (easy to prepare)

This traditional tart is such a nice dish for lunch. So light and savoury. It's perfect with watercress & crispy shallot salad.

500 g soft goats' cheese
100 ml single cream
1 egg & 2 yolks
23 cm short pastry case, blind-baked*
1 tbsp butter
1 garlic clove, crushed
200 g chestnut purée
200 ml vegetable stock
1 bay leaf

Preheat oven to 160°Cf. Roll the pastry into a pie dish and blind-bake. Set aside until ready to use.

For the chestnut layer, warm the butter and garlic in a pan and cook without colour then add the chestnut purée, stock and bay leaf. Simmer until reduced by half to a nice thick consistency. Spread into the tart case.

For the goats' cheese layer, remove any skin from the cheese then beat with the cream and eggs until light and smooth. Pour onto the chestnut layer and bake for 20 minutes or until set. Set aside to cool.

Serve cold or return to the oven to warm before serving.

Each portion provides 19g protein and 643kcals.

*see *The basics & extras,* page 285

nutrient	thumbs-up score
vitamin B6	👍👍👍👍
vitamin A total retinol equivalents)	👍👍👍
sodium	👍👍👍
chloride	👍👍👍
vitamin C	👍👍
iron	👍👍
folate	👍
thiamin	👍
calcium	👍
copper	👍
fibre (non-starch polysaccaride)	👍
magnesium	👍
phosphorus	👍
protein	👍
zinc	👍

Mushroom duxelle on melba toast ⚖

Serves 6-8 (medium difficulty to prepare)

Whether you're a vegetarian or not, these little chappies are little bundles of happiness. The Hollandaise isn't essential but it's delicious.

4 slices day-old bread
4 shallots (or 1 medium onion), finely chopped
a knob of butter
200 g mushrooms, finely chopped
1 tbsp Dijon mustard
salt & pepper
a dash of sriracha*
Hollandaise sauce*

Make the toast in advance. Remove the crusts from the bread slices then roll thin with a rolling pin. Cut into rounds with a scone cutter or simply cut into 5 cm squares and place on a baking sheet. Toast under the grill until lightly golden on both sides.

For the duxelle, grate the mushrooms with a food processor or cheese grater. Fry the shallots and butter until soft but without colour. Add the mushrooms and cook until the mixture has reduced and is quite dry. Add the mustard and sriracha and season to taste.

To assemble, drizzle Hollandaise on the toast and top with small quenelles of the duxelle as shown in the photo.

Each portion (4 pieces) provides 3g protein and 140kcals.

*see *The basics & extras,* page 285

nutrient	thumbs-up score
vitamin A (total retinol equivalents)	👍
vitamin B12	👍
sodium	👍
chloride	👍
copper	👍

Spanakopita & tzatziki

Yield 20 pieces (medium to advanced difficulty to prepare)

These were one of the first hors d'oeuvres I learned to make. I don't make them often enough. They're a perfect starter or great as a small bite.

For the spanakopita

500 g spinach, washed & shredded
a splash of olive oil
a dash of sriracha*
½ small onion, finely chopped
2 spring onions, finely chopped
100 g feta cheese
1 egg
1 tbsp Parmesan cheese, grated
a pinch of nutmeg
a few leaves of mint, chopped
salt & pepper
6 sheets of filo pastry
100 g butter, melted
fine bread crumbs

nutrient	thumbs-up score
vitamin A (total retinol equivalents)	>👍👍👍👍
sodium	👍👍👍👍
chloride	👍👍👍
vitamin B12	👍👍
vitamin C	👍👍
folate	👍👍
calcium	👍👍
riboflavin	👍👍
iron	👍
magnesium	👍
phosphorus	👍
potassium	👍
protein	👍

Heat the olive oil in a large pan and cook the onion and sriracha without colour. Add the spinach and warm until wilted. Tip into a colander and press out excess moisture. Return to the pan, add the spring onions and sauté for 1 minute. Crumble the feta cheese into a bowl then add the egg, Parmesan cheese, spinach, nutmeg and mint. Mix and season to taste.

Preheat oven to 180°Cf. Brush a sheet of filo with melted butter and lightly sprinkle with breadcrumbs. Place another layer on top and repeat with the rest of the sheets. Cut the filo stack into 7.5 cm strips then place a teaspoon of the spinach mixture in the middle of the strip. Fold the strip diagonally over the spinach then continue to gently fold the pastry to make triangular parcels. Brush the bottoms and tops with butter and place on a baking sheet. Bake for 20 to 30 minutes until crisp and golden. Serve immediately.

Each portion provides 16g protein and 520kcals.
* see *The Basics & extras,* page 285

For the tzatziki

3 tbsp olive oil
1 tbsp vinegar
2 cloves garlic, puréed
½ tsp salt
¼ tsp white pepper
225 g Greek set-style yoghurt
225 g soured cream
1 large cucumber peeled, de-seeded & chopped
1 tsp dill tops, finely chopped

nutrient	thumbs-up score
vitamin A (total retinol equivalents)	👍
magnesium	👍

Combine the olive oil, vinegar, garlic, salt, and pepper in a bowl. Whisk the yoghurt and sour cream together then add the oil mixture. Stir in the cucumber and dill and chill for two hours.

Each portion provides 4g protein and 190kcals.

Cheese grisini ⚖

Yields 12 large sticks (easy to prepare)

These are a fun little nibble and great to serve with pasta or soups. If you want to add to their nutritional value use whole grain flour.

(This is the same dough I use for pizza)

15 g fresh yeast or 1½ tsp dried yeast,
with a splash of warm water
250 g flour (*type 00* hard durum wheat or strong bread)
1 tsp salt
50 ml olive oil
225 g Parmesan or Emmenthal cheese, finely grated

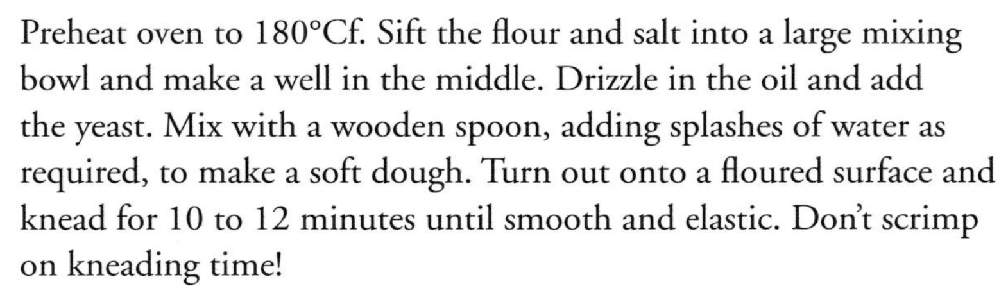

Preheat oven to 180°Cf. Sift the flour and salt into a large mixing bowl and make a well in the middle. Drizzle in the oil and add the yeast. Mix with a wooden spoon, adding splashes of water as required, to make a soft dough. Turn out onto a floured surface and knead for 10 to 12 minutes until smooth and elastic. Don't scrimp on kneading time!

Split the dough into 2 balls and place in a lightly oiled bowl, giving each ball a light coating of oil. Cover and leave in a warm place for about 1½ hours.

Flatten out the dough and knead again on a lightly floured surface for 2 to 3 minutes. At this stage you can wrap the dough and freeze for future use.

Roll out dough into 12 inch snakes. Brush lightly with olive oil and sprinkle with salt and finely grated Parmesan or Emmenthal cheese. Bake until golden and crisp.

Each portion provides 19g protein and 300kcals.

nutrient	thumbs-up score
vitamin B12	👍👍👍👍
calcium	👍👍👍
chloride	👍👍
phosphorus	👍👍
vitamin A (total retinol equivalents)	👍
folate	👍
copper	👍
iodine	👍
protein	👍
sodium	👍
zinc	👍

Roasted beetroot and goats' cheese salad, see page 145

Soups & salads

Soups

Prawn & ginger

Cream of cauliflower & cumin

Sweet pepper gazpacho with herb crostini

Creamy spiced butternut

Tuscan bean

Creamy watercress

Potato & leek potage

Sage, sweetcorn & onion chowder

White bean, sausage & kale

Nova Scotia clam chowder

Wild mushroom cappuccino

Salads

Caesar

Pearl cous cous, roasted tomato & asparagus

Mediterranean fennel

Pickled cucumber & dill

Roasted beetroot & goats' cheese

Spinach, watercress & crispy shallot

Greek

Moroccan carrot & orange

Cobb

Spinach

Comfort in a cup

Easy nourishment

You know, there are so many foods that can help make a nutritious start to your day. Superfoods? No such thing. It's a great way to describe foods that are generally good for us. Super ways of eating? Yes! That's what it's all about!

Soups and salads conjure up every idea and emotion we have about food – comfort, health, flavour, beauty and convenience. Just about every ingredient imaginable can become the centrepiece for a salad, sweet or savoury and there's nothing better than a cup of soup to sustain, cheer and nurture body and soul. Whether it's for winter warming or a palate refreshing chilled variety, soups offer the same ingredient options that salads do and you can enjoy them on the go – just pour from a flask.

Sometimes the aromas and even sight of cooked food on a plate can be a bit off-putting during treatment. Salads and chilled soups offer nutrition without the intensity of cooking aromas and soups are an easy way to get nutrition to simply slide past a sore throat or dry mouth.

It's a good idea to try new flavour combinations to encourage your appetite and soups can even be a way to take in foods you don't think you're going to enjoy but that you've heard might be good nutritional sources.

Take cruciferous vegetables as an example. Not everyone is a fan of cauliflower, Brussels sprouts, cabbage or horseradish but they're a great source of glucosinolates that have been shown in various studies to have cancer-fighting properties. And what about beans and pulses? Yes, chickpeas, lentils, baked beans, kidney beans, broad beans (fava). Perhaps they aren't to everyone's taste but zizzed up in a soup they provide a boost to your protein, B-vitamins and iron intake without a high fat content.

If you're trying to avoid weight gain during treatment, soups and salads can be filling without adding too much to your calorie intake.

Get moving

The housework workout

The more you involve yourself in everyday life, the fitter and happier you'll be, so turn mealtimes and snacks into a mini workout. There's even a scientific term for this:

NEPA, Non-Exercise Physical Activity.

Walking to and from the fridge is exercise. So is washing up and loading and unloading the dishwasher.

Stretching for items will help to loosen your chest, arms, torso and shoulders – include reaching sideways.

Tidying up and laying or clearing the table helps with co-ordination, while fetching and carrying (even something small and light) keeps your arm muscles working.

Just as every bite of food nourishes your body, every little movement stimulates your brain, circulation and muscles.

Looking good feels better

A bit about hands & feet, manicures & pedicures

Chemo and radiotherapy affects your hands and nails in the same way they do your hair because the treatment is designed to attack rapidly dividing cells. Your nails may become brittle, discoloured, indented or they may even bruise and fall off. Keeping your hands, feet and nails moisturised will help.

(While I think of it, also your elbows, knees and heels!)

Nail care is also an important consideration if you are managing lymphoedema, a condition that develops when lymph fluid accumulates in the soft tissue of the arm.

If you've had lymph nodes removed during surgery be careful of damage in and around nail beds, as bacteria can quickly lead to infection. Don't be tempted to rip or peel nails, rather cut carefully with clean nail scissors. Hygiene and gentle daily care are your best friends.

Prawn & ginger soup ⚖

Serves 4, (easy to prepare)

This is a wonderfully quick and delicious soup. Ginger is known to help with nausea, while the prawns deliver flavour, texture and much-needed trace elements.

12 whole prawns
1 clove garlic, finely chopped
2 stalks celery, finely chopped
5 cm piece of ginger, peeled
1 stalk of lemongrass, bruised
1 star anise
a bunch of fresh dill
500 ml chicken stock
250 ml water
a bunch of fresh chive, snipped
a bunch of fresh basil, chiffonade
salt & pepper
1 egg white (optional)

Chop half the ginger. Shell and de-vein the prawns. Put the shells and heads in a saucepan with the garlic, celery, chopped ginger, lemon grass, star anise and the stalks from the dill (save the sprigs). Pour in the stock and water, season lightly and simmer for 30 minutes.

Julienne the remaining ginger and finely chop the dill sprigs, chive and basil.

Next strain the liquid through a fine sieve into a clean pan. Add the prawns, ginger and herbs and simmer for a few minutes until the prawns are cooked. Season to taste.

Just before serving, gently beat the egg white with a fork but do not make it frothy. Pour into the hot soup and swirl with a fork to make threads. Serve immediately.

If you want a heartier soup add ramen noodles.

Each portion provides 6g protein and 33kcals.

nutrient	thumbs-up score
vitamin B12	>👍👍👍👍
sodium	👍👍
chloride	👍👍

Cream of cauliflower & cumin soup

Serves 4, (medium difficulty to prepare)

This soup is light and lovely anytime of year. It's a great and gentle way to get some essential vegetables and dairy.

3 onions, finely chopped
2 leeks, white only, finely sliced
550 ml milk
salt & white pepper
nutmeg
1 garlic clove, crushed
1 tsp cumin seeds
1 head of cauliflower, flourettes only
100 ml double cream
50 g grated Emmenthal

Warm the garlic in oil in a large, heavy saucepan then add the onions and leeks and cook without colour. Add the milk, salt and grate in some nutmeg. Put the cumin seeds in a small muslin sack* and suspend into the soup. Add the cauliflower and let simmer for 30 minutes.

Remove the cumin bag then liquidise the soup with a hand blender until smooth. If you want a very smooth, velvety soup pass it through a sieve then return to the heat to warm. Ladle the hot soup into bowls, top with grated cheese and grill to melt the cheese.

Each portion contains 17g protein and 440kcals.

* *Paper egg-poaching sacks work well for this and can be bought at most supermarkets.*

nutrient	thumbs-up score
vitamin B6	👍👍👍👍
vitamin B12	👍👍👍👍
vitamin C	👍👍👍👍
vitamin A (total retinol equivalents)	👍👍👍
calcium	👍👍👍
phosphorous	👍👍👍
folic acid	👍👍
thiamin	👍👍
iodine	👍👍
riboflavin	👍
copper	👍
fibre (as non-starch polysaccharide)	👍
iron	👍
magnesium	👍
potassium	👍
protein	👍
zinc	👍

Sweet pepper gazpacho with herb crostini

Serves 6 (easy to prepare)

This soup is a delightful low-fat recipe that brilliantly boosts your vitamin C intake. It's traditionally served chilled but it's equally good served hot. Either way the tomatoes and peppers are a perfect combination.

2 red sweet peppers
10 ml olive oil
1 onion, finely chopped
2 garlic cloves, crushed
a dash of sriracha*
675 g ripe tomatoes, chopped (fresh or tinned)
150 ml red wine
600 ml vegetable stock
salt & pepper
crème fraîche, croutons & chives for garnish

Cut the peppers into quarters and remove the white flesh and seeds. Brush lightly with olive oil and place skin-side up on a baking tray and place under the grill until the skins are well charred. Place in a plastic bag or covered bowl and allow to rest. When cool remove and discard the charred skin and chop into rough chunks.

Next coat a large pan with oil and add the onion, garlic and sriracha and cook without colour. Add the tomatoes and peppers and cook over medium low heat for 10 minutes. Add the wine and simmer for a further 5 minutes. Finally add the stock, check seasoning and simmer for 20 to 30 minutes.

Purée the soup with a hand mixer and pass through a sieve. Allow to chill for 2 to 3 hours. When chilled season to taste and garnish with a dollop of crème fraîche, croutons and chives.

Each portion with crostini provides 7g protein and 400kcals.

*see *The basics & extras*, page 285

nutrient	thumbs-up score
vitamin C	>👍👍👍👍
sodium	👍👍
chloride	👍
vitamin A (total retinol equivalents)	👍
vitamin B6	👍
folate	👍
calcium	👍
copper	👍
iron	👍
phosphorus	👍
selenium	👍

Creamy spiced butternut soup

Serves 4 (medium difficulty to prepare)

This is a lively soup that can wake up tired taste buds. The creaminess is easy on the tummy. It's also fast to prepare and freezes well.

4 rashers smoked bacon (optional)
50 g butter
a dash of sriracha*
1 medium onion, chopped
2 garlic cloves, chopped
900 g pumpkin or butternut squash
1 tbsp coriander seeds
2 tsp cumin seeds
2 small dried chillies
1 litre chicken or vegetable stock
100 ml coconut cream
salt & pepper

Fry the bacon until very crisp and break into bits. Set aside to use as garnish.

Melt the butter in a large saucepan, add the sriracha and cook the onion and garlic without colour.

Peel and de-seed the pumpkin. Remove the stringy bits as well. Chop into 2 inch cubes then add to the onion. Cook until the pumpkin is lightly golden and softening.

In a separate pan toast the coriander and cumin seeds over a low heat for about 2 minutes. They will release a lovely perfume. Place in a mortar, add the chillies and grind to a fine consistency. Add the spices to the pumpkin and cook for 1 minute.

Now add the stock and simmer for 20 minutes or until the pumpkin is tender.

Pour in most of the cream and blitz with a hand blender until smooth.

Heat again until piping hot. Season to taste. Garnish with a drizzle of cream and bacon bits if using and serve hot.

Each portion provides 11g and 280kcals.

* see *The basics & extras,* page 285

*** Toasted pumpkin seeds make a great snack. Wash the seeds, place them on a tray, sprinkle with salt then roast in a medium oven (180°Cf) until lightly toasted. They're morish.*

nutrient	thumbs-up score
vitamin B6	>👍👍👍👍
sodium	👍👍👍👍
chloride	👍👍👍
thiamin	👍👍
vitamin A	👍👍
vitamin C	👍👍
calcium	👍
iron	👍
phosphorus	👍
protein	👍

Tuscan bean soup

Serves 4 (medium difficulty to prepare)

This is a grand Italian tradition. As with all classics there's no 'right way' so feel free to adjust to your taste. Try adding some braised cabbage or a bit of pasta.

2 tbsp olive oil
a dash of sriracha*
2 garlic cloves, peeled & crushed
2 onions, chopped
2 leeks, chopped
2 carrots, chopped
4 sprigs of thyme
2 to 3 sprigs fresh rosemary
2 bay leaves
1 litre vegetable stock
juice of ½ a lemon
400 g chopped tomatoes
1 tin cannellini beans
1 tin borlotti beans
300 g spicy Italian sausage, (approx. 4 links)
a bunch of parsley, chopped
50 g Parmesan cheese, finely grated
salt & pepper

Heat the oil in a large saucepan and gently cook the garlic, onions, leeks and carrots until soft. Add thyme, rosemary, bay leaves, stock, lemon juice and tomatoes and simmer for 20 minutes. Add the beans and some chopped parsley. Season to taste and continue to simmer for another 10 minutes.

In a separate pan grill the sausages. When cooked, remove the meat from casings, crumble then set aside.

Ladle 1½ cups of the soup into a separate pan and purée using a hand blender then re-introduce into the soup and add the sausage. This will give the soup body without making it too thick. Season to taste.

Garnish with grated Parmesan cheese and serve hot with crusty bread.

Each portion provides 31g protein and 600kcals.

*see *The basics & extras,* page 285

nutrient	thumbs-up score
vitamin A (total retinol equivalents)	>👍👍👍👍
vitamin B6	>👍👍👍👍
vitamin B12	👍👍👍👍
sodium	👍👍👍👍
chloride	👍👍👍👍
thiamin	👍👍👍
iron	👍👍👍
phosphorus	👍👍👍
folate	👍👍
potassium	👍👍
protein	👍👍
zinc	👍👍
niacin	👍
riboflavin	👍
calcium	👍
copper	👍
magnesium	👍
selenium	👍

Creamy watercress soup

Serves 4 (easy to prepare)

Watercress is naturally quite salty and peppery in flavour so take care not to over-season. If you don't want the dairy, use extra stock – it's just as delicious.

50 g butter
450 g leek, white only, washed & sliced
2 bunches watercress, chopped
1 medium potato, peeled & chopped
1 litre vegetable stock (more if not using cream)
150 ml double cream (optional)
salt & pepper

Melt the butter on a low heat in a deep, heavy saucepan. Add the vegetables (save a few watercress leaves for garnish) and sweat without colour until softened but still firm.

Pour in the stock and simmer on low heat for about 10 minutes. Remove from the heat and allow to cool. If the mixture is thicker than you want, add more stock. Liquidise the cooled soup. The mixture should be a dark, rich green. Set a small amount aside and return the rest to the saucepan.

Now stir in the cream if desired.

Season to taste and reheat gently. To serve, ladle into a wide bowl then swirl some of the reserved dark soup around it.

Each portion provides 5g protein and 350kcals.

nutrient	thumbs-up score
vitamin A (total retinol equivalents)	>👍👍👍👍
vitamin B6	>👍👍👍👍
vitamin C	>👍👍👍👍
sodium	👍👍
chloride	👍
thiamin	👍
calcium	👍
fibre (as non-starch polysaccharide)	👍
folate	👍
iron	👍
magnesium	👍
phosphorus	👍

Potato & leek potage ⚖

Serves 4 (medium difficulty to prepare)

This soup has soul. It is so nourishing and easy on digestion. The bright colour is tantalising and its creaminess makes it perfect comfort food.

6 to 8 large floury potatoes
2 to 3 litres chicken or vegetable stock
a dash of sriracha*
1 egg yolk
3 leeks, whites only, finely chopped
1 tsp turmeric
½ tsp fennel seed
croutons*
a small bunch of fresh parsley, finely chopped
a pinch of nutmeg
salt & pepper

Peel and boil the potatoes in the stock with a drop of sriracha. Drain, reserving the stock, then purée with the egg yolk and nutmeg. Season to taste.

Sauté the leeks in olive oil until soft. Add half the potato purée, turmeric and fennel seed and whiz in a food processor gradually adding stock to achieve a creamy consistency. Season to taste and keep warm.

Spoon an island of potato purée into the centre of a bowl then surround with the leek pottage. Garnish with croutons, parsley and nutmeg. Serve hot.

Each portion provides 7g protein and 180kcals.

*see *The basics & extras*, page 285

nutrient	thumbs-up score
vitamin B6	>👍👍👍👍
sodium	👍👍👍👍
chloride	👍👍👍
thiamin	👍👍
vitamin A	👍👍
vitamin C	👍
calcium	👍
iron	👍
phosphorus	👍
protein	👍

Sage, sweetcorn & onion chowder

Serves 4 (medium difficulty to prepare)

This is a savoury gem. The sage, bacon and onion remain individual flavours that complement each other. If you prefer plant-based, replace the bacon with mushrooms. It's a lovely warming dish.

60 g butter
4 white onions, thinly sliced
200 g sweetcorn
2 garlic cloves, crushed
4 smoked bacon rashers
2 tbsp flour
1 litre vegetable stock
300 ml single cream
5 waxy potatoes, diced into fine cubes
1 tbsp fresh sage, finely chopped
2 tbsp white wine vinegar
a few fresh sage leaves, chiffonade
salt & pepper

In a large frying pan, sauté the onions and garlic in butter ensuring to cook them without colour. Add the bacon and continue to sauté until cooked and the onions are slightly caramelised then stir in the flour and sauté for an additional minute and set aside.

Next place stock, onions and potatoes in a pot, season and simmer for about 20 minutes until the potatoes are cooked but still firm. Add the cream and sweetcorn and bring back to the boil. Finally, add the sage and vinegar. Season to taste. Garnish with sage leaves and serve hot.

Each portion provides 14g protein and 530kcals.

nutrient	thumbs-up score
sodium	>👍👍👍👍
chloride	👍👍👍👍
vitamin B6	👍👍👍👍
vitamin A total retinol equivalents)	👍👍
vitamin B12	👍👍
thiamin	👍👍
phosphorus	👍👍
calcium	👍
copper	👍
fibre (non-starch polysaccaride)	👍
folate	👍
potassium	👍
protein	👍

White bean, sausage & kale soup

Serves 4 (medium difficulty to prepare)

This soup is a bit of a 'big fella' – a real meal on its own. I'm always looking for ways to sneak a few more beans into our diet.

350 g extra-lean sausage meat
470 g (2 tins) cannellini beans, drained & rinsed
1 tbsp olive oil
a dash of sriracha*
1 white onion, chopped
1 litre chicken stock
1 tbsp red wine vinegar
small bunch of curly kale or collards, finely chopped
salt & pepper

Brown the sausage meat in a lightly oiled pan.

Thoroughly rinse the beans, place them in a bowl and roughly mash.

Then in a lightly oiled deep, heavy pan, soften the onion and sriracha then add the stock and beans. Allow to simmer on medium heat for about 30 minutes then blitz with a hand blender until smooth. Pass the mixture through a sieve and return to the pot then stir in the vinegar and add the sausage. Bring to the boil to allow the soup to simmer for a further 30 minutes and season to taste. Finally add the chopped greens and cook on low heat until the greens are soft, about 30 minutes.

As the soup reduces and thickens add water to achieve desired consistency.

Serve hot.

Each portion provides 24g protein and 320kcals.

*see *The basics & extras,* page 285

nutrient	thumbs-up score
vitamin A (total retinol equivalents)	>👍👍👍👍
vitamin C	>👍👍👍👍
sodium	>👍👍👍👍
chloride	>👍👍👍👍
fibre (non-starch polysaccaride)	👍👍👍
phosphorus	👍👍👍
vitamin B6	👍👍
folate	👍👍
calcium	👍👍
iron	👍👍
protein	👍👍
copper	👍
potassium	👍
magnesium	👍
zinc	👍

Nova Scotia clam chowder

Serves 4, (medium difficulty to prepare)

This maritime classic is a hearty warming meal and a great source of complete protein. The cream base makes it a good source of calcium. It's easy on the tummy too.

100 g smoked bacon rashers
1 onion, chopped
1 stalk celery, chopped
350 ml boiling water
4 medium waxy potatoes, diced
300 g small clams, fresh or tinned (2 tins drained weight)
milk
120 ml single cream
3 tsp butter
1 tsp celery salt
salt & pepper

Fry the bacon until crisp in a large saucepan then remove, dry and break into bits. Next add the onions and celery to the drippings and cook without colour. Add the boiling water and potatoes and boil until just tender. This should take about 10 minutes. Drain the clams over a jug and top up the clam liquid with milk to make 1 litre and add this to the potatoes.

Gently simmer then add the clams, cooked bacon, cream, butter and seasoning. Heat until the broth is creamy. Be careful not to boil.

Serve hot.

Each portion provides 22g protein and 300kcals.

nutrient	thumbs-up score
vitamin B6	>👍👍👍👍
sodium	>👍👍👍👍
chloride	>👍👍👍👍
iron	👍👍👍
phosphorus	👍👍
vitamin B12	👍👍
copper	👍👍
protein	👍👍
vitamin A (total retinol equivalents)	👍
niacin	👍
thiamin	👍
calcium	👍
potassium	👍
zinc	👍

Wild mushroom cappuccino

Serves 4, (easy to medium difficulty to prepare)

This vegetarian soup has everything. It's packed with nutrition, freezes in small portions and most of all, it's packed with flavour and fun. Wild dried porcini are easily available and give an intense flavour finish.

800 g chestnut or cup mushrooms
1 medium red onion
2 shallots
1 clove garlic, smashed
olive oil
1 litre vegetable stock
250 ml single cream (optional)
1 tbsp thyme leaves, finely chopped
a dash of sriracha*
salt & pepper
50 ml milk
a few dried porcini

Grate the mushrooms with a cheese grater and finely chop the onions and shallots.

Next, lightly coat a large frying pan with olive oil then add the mushrooms. Leave on a low heat and allow the mushrooms to fry until the moisture is gone. This will take 30 to 40 minutes. Add the onion, shallots, garlic, sriracha and thyme. Continue on low heat until the onions and shallots are cooked through.

Transfer the mixture into a pan on medium heat and add the stock. Cover and let simmer for 20 to 30 minutes. Add the cream then continue to simmer until the soup is a nice consistency – not too watery but not too thick.

Cream the soup using a hand blender then pass through a sieve. Return to the pan to keep warm and season to taste. If the soup gets thick, thin with a bit of water.

To make the cappuccino dust, place the dried porcini in a coffee bean grinder and whiz into to a fine dust. Pass through a sieve. When ready to serve, make cappuccino milk foam by heating milk in a pan to scalding being careful not to boil. Whisk continuously so the milk develops into a thick foam.

To serve, pour the soup into a cup and top with foamed milk as you would a cappuccino. Dust with the porcini powder and serve immediately.

Each portion provides 8g protein and 200kcals.

*see *The basics & extras,* page 285

nutrient	thumbs-up score
copper	>👍👍👍👍
sodium	👍👍👍
chloride	👍👍
phosphorus	👍👍
vitamin A (total retinol equivalents)	👍
vitamin B6	👍
vitamin B12	👍
niacin	👍
riboflavin	👍
folate	👍
iron	👍
potassium	👍
selenium	👍

Caesar salad

Serves 4 (easy to prepare)

I've chosen the original recipe because its a winner for vitamin B12 served on its own. It has wonderful crunchy texture and aroma and the strong flavours can really help wake up sleeping tastebuds.

1 garlic clove, whole
2 heads romaine lettuce, torn
small anchovies
croutons*
½ cup Parmesan cheese, finely grated
black pepper

Dressing

2 garlic cloves, crushed
juice of 1 lemon
olive oil
2 egg yolks
1 tsp Worcestershire sauce
1 tsp dry mustard
salt & pepper

Cut the garlic in two and rub the cut halves over the inside of a wooden salad bowl to season. Add the dressing ingredients and whisk together. Add the lettuce, anchovies and croutons and toss to combine. Sprinkle over the cheese and finish with a generous amount of black pepper.

Each portion provides 10g protein and 400kcals.

*see *The basics & extras*, page 285

nutrient	thumbs-up score:
vitamin B12	>👍👍👍👍
vitamin B6	👍👍
sodium	👍👍
chloride	👍👍
calcium	👍
phosphorus	👍

Pearl cous cous, roasted tomato & asparagus salad

Serves 6 (easy to medium difficulty to prepare)

Pearl cous cous is also called 'giant or Israeli cous cous'. It's actually pasta and a diverse alternative in salad or served as a hot side dish. For this simple salad you can use any veg or add a bit of feta or buffalo mozzarella.

250 g pearl cous cous
2 litres vegetable stock
8 to 10 cherry tomatoes
8 to 10 fine asparagus tips
1 shallot, very finely chopped
olive oil
a dash of balsamic vinegar
juice & zest of 1 lemon
a small bunch of flat leaf parsley, chopped
salt & pepper
a handful of grated Parmesan, (optional)
a few basil leaves

Boil the cous cous in the vegetable stock for 5 minutes or until the pearls are al dente. Rinse well and toss with a light splash of olive oil.

Preheat oven to 180°Cf. Give the tomatoes a light coating of olive oil and pop a drop or two of balsamic vinegar on the tops then place on a baking tray. Bake them for about 5 minutes. Just when the skin starts to split remove them from the oven.

Trim the asparagus and steam until tender but firm and drain on a piece of kitchen roll.

Mix together the lemon juice, zest and enough olive oil to lightly dress the salad. Season to taste.

Toss all the ingredients and dressing in with the cous cous and garnish with a few shredded basil leaves. Allow to chill for a few hours before serving.

If you are adding cheese do this when ready to serve.

Each portion provides 3g protein and 100kcals.

nutrient	thumbs-up score
vitamin C	👍
sodium	👍
chloride	👍
iron	👍
phosphorus	👍

Mediterranean fennel salad

Serves 4 (easy to prepare)

Fresh, simple and crunchy. This is a great accompaniment for fish.

1 fennel bulb
6 breakfast radishes
a handful of French beans
½ a cucumber
a few fresh dill tops, finely chopped
zest of 1 lemon
1 tsp lemon juice
3 tbsp olive oil
salt & pepper

nutrient	thumbs-up score
sodium	👍
chloride	👍
vitamin C (18% RNI)	nearly 👍

Finely shred the fennel, slice the radish and julienne the beans. Remove the seeds and slice the cucumber into small sticks. Mix the vegetables together adding the dill and lemon zest. Mix together the oil and lemon and a bit of seasoning and mix into the salad.

Each portion provides 1g protein and 15kcals.

Pickled cucumber & dill salad

Serves 4 (easy to prepare)

Northern Europeans serve this fresh salad with fish, rye bread and cheese.

1 large cucumber, thinly sliced
1 large white onion, thinly sliced
75 ml cider vinegar
a pinch of caster sugar
3 tbsp fresh dill tops, chopped
salt & pepper

nutrient	thumbs-up score
On its own this salad doesn't rate a score. It's low in calories and has bags of flavour to wake up tired taste buds and the cucumber is soothing.	

Place the cucumber and onion slices in a bowl and sprinkle with salt. Let stand for 10 minutes. Add the vinegar and sugar, a drizzle of cold water and dill. Toss until nicely mixed and chill for a few hours.

Each portion provides 1g protein and 25kcals.

Roasted beetroot & goats' cheese salad

See illustration on page 114

Serves 6 (easy to prepare)

I think this is a real beauty. The colour is lovely. The flavour mixture is divine and it's so very easy to prepare.

4 large or 8 baby beetroot,
  rinsed & trimmed
1 tbsp olive oil
salt & pepper
1 shallot, julienned
Dijon vinaigrette*
10 cups mesclun salad**
250 g goats' cheese, cubed
a handful of walnuts or pecans

Preheat oven to 200°Cf. Place the beetroot in a roasting tin, drizzle with the olive oil and season. Cover with foil and roast for 25 minutes, then uncover and roast for a further 15 minutes or until fork-tender. Allow the beetroots to cool then peel, slice and place in a medium bowl with the shallot and drizzle with Dijon vinaigrette.

Place on a bed of mesclun salad and top with goats' cheese. Sprinkle with walnuts or pecans and serve.

If you don't want to faff about with the beetroot, buy pre-cooked and rinse well.

Each portion provides 18g protein and 545kcals.

*see *The basics & extras*, page 285

*** mesclun salad – the term comes from the South of France, meaning 'mixed'. It's a combination of young sweet, bitter and spicy leaves such as: mizuna; oak leaf lettuce; dandelion; Swiss chard; rocket (arugula); chervil; mustard greens; beetroot greens; endive and others. It is now easily bought pre-packaged.*

nutrient	thumbs-up score
vitamin B6	👍👍👍👍
sodium	👍👍👍
chloride	👍👍👍
vitamin C	👍👍
folate	👍👍
phosphorus	👍👍
vitamin A total retinol equivalents)	👍
vitamin B12	👍
riboflavin	👍
calcium	👍
copper	👍
iodine	👍
magnesium	👍
protein	👍
iron	👍
zinc	👍

Spinach, watercress & crispy shallot salad

Serves 6 to 8 (easy to prepare)

This big peppery salad is great on its own or with a tart or creamed gazpacho.

For the salad

olive oil
5 large shallots, peeled & cut into rings
flour
milk
150 g watercress, stalks removed
150 g baby spinach leaves, washed & stalks removed

For the vinaigrette

3 tbsp olive oil
1 tbsp red wine vinegar
1 tbsp Dijon mustard
1 tbsp créme fraîche
salt & pepper
a few chives, finely chopped

For the crispy shallots, heat enough oil in a pan to deep-fry. Place the rings into the hot oil until golden then remove with the slotted spoon and drain on kitchen roll. They are quite delicate so it only takes a minute. In the meantime, prepare beds of spinach and watercress on plates, mix together the dressing ingredients and season to taste. Arrange the shallot rings on the salad, drizzle with dressing and garnish with spikes of chive.

Each portion provides 4g protein and 220kcals.

nutrient	thumbs-up score
vitamin C	👍👍
vitamin A (total retinol equivalents)	👍

Greek salad

Serves 4 to 6 (easy to prepare)

This is a salad to enjoy with all your senses. It's so bright and full of texture and packed with vitamins. To enhance the texture and aroma use a variety of tomatoes. It's perfect with Spanikopita and Simon's Pie.

For the dressing

1 garlic clove, crushed
2 tsp red wine vinegar
2 tsp of olive oil
a dash of sriracha*
salt & pepper

For the salad

600 g tomatoes (baby plum, beef, vine ripened pomadoro)
½ a red onion finely sliced
½ a green pepper, finely sliced
70 g pitted black olives
juice of ½ a lemon
200 g of feta cheese
a handful of fresh oregano

Slice the tomatoes into a variety of shapes, add the onion and the pepper rings and squeeze the olives into your hands to drop into the salad. Crumble the feta cheese on top and add lemon juice. Drizzle on the dressing and top with the sprigs of oregano.

Smash the clove of garlic and add to vinegar, sriracha and oil. Season to taste.

Each portion provides 10g protein and 200kcals.

*see *The basics & extras,* page 285

nutrient	thumbs-up score:
vitamin B6	>👍👍👍👍
sodium	>👍👍👍👍
chloride	>👍👍👍👍
vitamin C	👍👍👍👍
vitamin A (total retinol equivalents)	👍👍
vitamin B12	👍👍
calcium	👍
folate	👍
phosphorus	👍

Moroccan carrot & orange salad

Serves 6 (easy to prepare)

Inspired by the North African sunshine this salad is full of zest & flavour.

450 g carrots
2 large oranges
seeds of 1 pomegranate
mesclun salad (see page 145)
1 tbsp olive oil
juice & zest of 1 lemon
a pinch of sugar
½ tsp ground cumin
½ tsp ground cinnamon
a handful of pine nuts, toasted
salt & pepper

Trim, peel and roughly grate the carrots. Peel the oranges over a bowl removing the white pith and seeds and catching any juice then cut into bite-sized slices. Whisk together the olive oil, orange juice, pinch of sugar, cumin and cinnamon. Carefully add the lemon juice and zest and season to taste. Toss the carrots, orange slices, pomegranate seeds and pine nuts in a bowl and toss with dressing. Serve chilled.

De-seeding a pomegranate is easy. Simply halve the fruit along the equator then old each half, seed-side down over a bowl of cold water and tap the shell with a spoon. The seeds will drop out with ease.

Each portion provides 2g protein and 100kcals.

nutrient	thumbs-up score
vitamin A (total retinol equivalents)	>👍👍👍👍
vitamin C	👍👍👍
sodium	👍
chloride	👍

Cobb salad

Serves 4 (medium difficulty to prepare)

The original was first presented at Hollywood's Brown Derby restaurant by its owner, Robert H Cobb. The jury is out whether he used smoked turkey or chicken. Either way, it's an enduring American classic.

½ head iceberg lettuce
a small bunch of watercress
a bunch of endive (chicory)
½ head romaine lettuce
2 medium tomatoes, de-seeded & chopped
225 g smoked turkey breast, diced
6 rashers bacon, crispy & diced
1 avocado, peeled & sliced
3 eggs, hardboiled & diced
a small bunch of chives, finely chopped
100 g blue cheese, crumbled
a baguette to serve

For the vinaigrette

2 tbsp water
½ tsp sugar
a pinch of sea salt
½ tsp Worcestershire sauce
2 tbsp balsamic vinegar
1 tbsp lemon juice
½ tsp fresh ground black pepper
½ tsp Dijon mustard
½ cup olive oil (or more to taste)
2 garlic cloves, puréed

Place the serving bowls in the fridge or freezer. Finely chop all the greens, (chiffonade), and arrange them in rows on a chilled salad platter.

Finely dice and chop the rest of the ingredients and arrange them in rows across the greens. Sprinkle with the chives and keep refrigerated until ready to serve.

Serve with chilled salad bowls and present the dressing on the side with a basket of sliced baguette and butter.

For the vinaigrette, combine all the ingredients except the olive oil in a blender then with the machine running, drizzle in the oil and blend well. It will store well in a sealed container in the refrigerator.

Each portion provides 34g protein and 940kcals.

nutrient	thumbs-up score
vitamin B6	>👍👍👍👍
sodium	>👍👍👍👍
chloride	👍👍👍👍
vitamin B12	👍👍👍
thiamin	👍👍👍
phosphorus	👍👍👍
protein	👍👍👍
niacin	👍👍
vitamin A (total retinol equivalents)	👍
vitamin C	👍
riboflavin	👍
calcium	👍
copper	👍
fibre (as non-starch polysaccharide)	👍
folate	👍
iron	👍
magnesium	👍
potassium	👍
selenium	👍
zinc	👍

Spinach salad

Serves 4 (easy to prepare)

This recipe is based on the original classic. The bacon bits pop up like little nuggets of happiness. Uncooked spinach provides a healthy daily portion of iron, so it's good when watching for anemia.

250 - 300 g young spinach leaves, washed
2 eggs, hard-boiled & sliced
4 rashers crisp streaky bacon, grilled & crumbled
4 button mushrooms, finely sliced

For the dressing

1 tbsp grainy Dijon mustard
1 handful fresh basil, chopped
1 tsp coarsely cracked black pepper
2 large shallots, finely chopped
2 egg yolks
80 ml balsamic vinegar
250 ml olive oil
a dash of Worcestershire sauce
salt & pepper

Place the mustard, basil, black pepper, shallots, egg yolks, Worcestershire sauce and vinegar in a blender. Blend on a high speed and slowly add the oil. Add a little water if the mixture becomes too thick. Season to taste with the remaining ingredients. One helpful hint is that if the vinegar overpowers the dressing you can add a little sugar to balance the flavour.

Wash and dry the spinach leaves and lay out on a plate. Add the sliced egg, bacon and mushrooms and drizzle with dressing.

Each portion provides 12g protein and 620kcals.

nutrient	thumbs-up score
vitamin B6	>👍👍👍👍
vitamin A (total retinol equivalents)	👍👍👍
vitamin B12	👍👍👍
sodium	👍👍👍
chloride	👍👍👍
folate	👍
iodine	👍
iron	👍
phosphorus	👍
protien	👍

Courgette bread see page 167

Afternoon tea

Grazing
Afternoon tea

When you're undergoing treatment, so many things can sap your interest in food.

Sometimes the mere thought of a sit-down meal can result in you losing the desire to eat during treatment. Different medicines can have different side-effects but thankfully, most are short-term and go once treatment has finished. All the same, you may have to get through times when your mouth gets dry or becomes sensitive to rough textures or your tastebuds change causing food to taste metallic, plasticky or cardboard-like so a bit of creativity with flavours and textures can be helpful. You may have to manage nausea, sickness or just tiredness so trying 'little and often' throughout the day can help keep your nutritional intake up. As you notice your preferences changing, why not experiment a little?

Frequently it can be the tastes that you don't think you're going to enjoy that become a new taste sensation and favourite flavour. Try not to rule anything out and be open to a bit of trial and error when it comes to what makes your tastebuds tingle. Try small amounts to eat and drink all the same.

Of course, afternoon snacks come in a great variety and are part of every culture. The Spanish have tapas, the Italians have antipasti and the English have afternoon tea. Something to stimulate the appetite and wake up our desire for food might be just what you need!

It's a lovely tradition that offers endless ideas for making 'little and often' work for you. Here are a few ideas.

Get moving
Muscle up

Mid to late afternoon is the best time to work your muscles, as strength and endurance are at their peak. The afternoon is also when reaction time is quickest and heart rate and blood pressure are lowest. That all means getting stronger should be easier.

Your main focus should be on exercises that translate into everyday activities, such as sitting down and getting up from the sofa, getting in and out of the bath or carrying bags of shopping. You also need to strengthen your stomach, sides and back, as inactivity can lead to back problems.

Don't worry about special equipment – your own body weight and small bottles of water or cans of veg will do to start with, although some items, such as balance cushions and light weights can also be helpful.

If you were a gym bunny before diagnosis, you can adapt your regular exercises but do take expert advice, start with low weights and repetitions and build up gradually.

You'll find some ideas on page 308.

Looking good feels better
Let's face it

Your face and lips can take a real beating during treatment and can become hypersensitive and prone to rash. Your skin can weaken and bruise easily and your lips don't have melanin or sweat glands, so can be extra sensitive to sunlight, which means they might dry and split.

Try introducing a few simple things such as sleeping on your back with your head slightly elevated to relieve puffiness, which can startle us all when we look in the morning mirror. Also, be generous with sun block – you really want to protect your skin from further exposure to UVA and UVB light (and ladies – watch that cleavage as well!).

Finally, moisturise, moisturise, moisturise! Choose gentle soaps and lotions. Ask your pharmacist about antibacterial and paraffin-based bath and shower emollients. These are designed for people with ultra-sensitive skin conditions such as psoriasis and eczema.

Cranberry teacakes

Yield 18-24 muffins (easy to prepare)

These are so morish. Sweet and a bit tangy at the same time. If you use fresh cranberries coarsely chop them and add a bit more milk so the batter isn't too stiff to spoon out.

500 ml flour
125 ml sugar
4 tsp baking powder
½ tsp salt
2 eggs
50 ml sunflower oil
125 ml milk
250 ml whole cranberry sauce
 (or fresh cranberries, coarsely chopped)
a knob of butter

Preheat oven to 170°Cf and grease muffin tins (if not using muffin liners).

Sift together flour, sugar, baking powder and salt into a bowl and make a well in the middle.

In a separate bowl whisk the eggs until frothy then stir in the oil, milk and cranberry sauce or cranberries. Pour the mixture into the well and stir with a spoon until fully moistened but still lumpy. Don't over stir. If the mixture is dry add a bit more milk.

Fill the tins to ¾ full and bake for 20 to 25 minutes until a toothpick comes out clean. Remove from the oven, brush with melted butter and sprinkle with sugar.

Each portion (2 teacakes) provides 9g protein and 450kcals.

(Adding a preserve, marmalade, butter or cream will significantly increase the nutritional value and yum factor.)

nutrient	thumbs-up score
2 teacakes provide	
vitamin B12	👍
phosphorus	👍
potassium	👍

Mom's sour cream cake

Yield 1 cake, 9 pieces (easy to medium difficulty to prepare)

This recipe always brings back lovely memories of sitting in my mother's kitchen with a cup of coffee. Her table was always full of friends and family and this cake was in great demand.

For the cake batter

1½ cups caster sugar
¾ cup butter, softened
3 eggs
1½ tsp vanilla extract
3 cups flour
1½ tsp baking powder
1½ tsp baking soda
¾ tsp salt
1½ cups sour cream

For the filling

½ cup packed brown sugar
½ cup walnuts, finely chopped
1½ tsp cinnamon

For the glaze

¼ cup brown butter*
2 cups icing sugar
1 tsp vanilla extract
2 tbsp milk

Preheat oven to 170°Cf and grease and flour a 23 cm tin (or bundt tin)

Cream together the butter, sugar and 1 egg until fluffy. Beat in the other eggs until smooth. Sift the flour, soda, baking powder and salt into a separate bowl. Beat into the wet mixture alternately with portions of sour cream until fully mixed and smooth. Pour half the batter into the tin.

Mix together the brown sugar, cinnamon and nuts then sprinkle over the batter. Spoon in the remaining batter and bake for 45 minutes to 1 hour or until a toothpick comes out clean.

Prepare the glaze by mixing all the ingredients into a bowl and stirring until completely smooth.

When the cake is baked, remove from the tin while warm and place on a plate. Drizzle with glaze and allow to cool.

Each portion provides 10g protein and 910kcals.

* see *The basics & extras,* page 285

nutrient	thumbs-up score
vitamin A (total retinol equivalents)	👍👍👍
vitamin B12	👍👍
phosphorus	👍👍
sodium	👍👍
chloride	👍
calcium	👍
copper	👍
iodine	👍
iron	👍

Me-oh my-oh moreos

Yield: about 32 sandwich cookies (medium difficulty to prepare)

Who can resist an oreo cookie? I've given the quantities in both American and metric measures because sometimes 'a cup of this and half cup of that' is just easier.

125 g (1¼ cups) cocoa powder
235 g (1½ cups) all-purpose flour,
plus more for dusting
½ tsp baking powder
¼ tsp salt
230 g (1 cup) butter, softened
365 g (1½ cups) granulated sugar
100 g (½ cup) light brown sugar, packed
1 large egg, plus 1 yolk
1 tsp vanilla extract
½ tsp instant coffee, dissolved
in ½ tsp warm water
450 g (1 package) rolling fondant icing
a bit of icing sugar for rolling
a bit of milk

Sift together the cocoa, flour, baking powder and salt. In a large bowl, cream together the butter, sugar and brown sugar. Mix in the egg and yolk one at a time, then the vanilla, followed by the instant coffee, mixing in each ingredient before adding the next. Add the dry ingredients to make a smooth dough. Divide the dough into halves (about 550 g each), wrap in cling film and chill for 1 hour.

Knead the dough slightly to soften and prevent cracking when rolling. Place each piece between 2 sheets of cling film and roll to 1 to 1.5 cm thickness. Using a 5 cm round cookie cutter, cut the dough into rounds. If you need to, re-chill the scraps before you re-roll them. Place the cookies about 2 inches apart on parchment-lined baking sheets. Chill for 20 minutes.

Preheat the oven to 160°Cf. Bake the cookies for 20 minutes or until they are just set. Take care as if they get too dark or burn the chocolate will become bitter. Cool completely.

To build the sandwiches, roll out the fondant, between sheets of cling film to 1.5 cm thickness and cut into circles using the same cookie cutter as for the cookies. Brush one side of the fondant with a little milk and press on a cookie. Turn them over, brush with a bit more milk and press on another cookie. Voila!

Each portion (1 sandwich cookie) provides 2g protein and 200 kcals.

nutrient thumbs-up score

These are not nutritional giants but they are truly delicious.

Carrot loaf

Yields 1 loaf, 8 slices (easy to prepare)

I love breads and cakes made from vegetables. They're so perfect with a cuppa.

125 ml sunflower oil
2 eggs
1 cup carrots, finely grated
425 ml flour
2 tsp baking powder
½ tsp baking soda
1 tsp cinnamon
¾ tsp ground nutmeg
¼ tsp ground clove
¼ tsp ginger
125 ml walnuts, chopped (optional)

Preheat oven to 170°Cf and grease and flour a 23 cm loaf tin.

Beat the oil, eggs and sugar together until well blended then stir in the carrots. In a separate bowl mix the remaining ingredients. Pour into the batter and stir until just moistened. Turn into the loaf tin and bake for approximately 1 hour or until a toothpick comes out clean. Allow to cool in the tin for 10 minutes before removing.

Each portion provides 9g protein and 450kcals.

nutrient	thumbs-up score
phosphorus	👍👍
vitamin A (total retinol equivalents)	👍
vitamin B12	👍
copper	👍

Courgette bread — see illustration on page 156

Yields 1 loaf, 8 slices (easy to prepare)

This is simply scrumptious served hot with lashings of butter or cream cheese.

2 eggs
½ cup sunflower oil
1 cup granulated sugar
1 cup courgette, grated
1 tsp vanilla extract
2 cups flour
1 tsp baking powder
1 tsp baking soda
½ tsp salt
1 tsp cinnamon

Preheat oven to 170°Cf and grease and flour a 23 cm loaf tin.

Beat the eggs in a bowl until light and frothy, add the oil and sugar and beat until smooth. Add the courgette and vanilla. In another bowl combine the flour, baking powder, soda, salt and cinnamon. Fold in the courgette mixture. Pour into the tin and bake for 50 to 60 minutes or until a toothpick comes out clean.

Each portion provides 5g protein and 370kcals.

nutrient	thumbs-up score
phosphorus	👍👍
vitamin A (total retinol equivalents)	👍
vitamin B12	👍
copper	👍

Orange cake

Yield 1, 22 cm cake, serves 8 (medium difficulty to prepare)

This is about the juiciest cake on the planet! It's a cake that puts a smile on your face. Make it for someone you love.

250 ml butter, softened
250 g caster sugar
4 eggs
zest of 1 orange
250 g self-raising flour
85 ml freshly squeezed orange juice

For the icing

125 g icing sugar
5 tsp freshly squeezed orange juice

Preheat oven to 160°Cf and grease and line a 22 cm round cake tin with baking parchment.

Cream the butter and sugar together for 3 to 4 minutes, until pale and fluffy. Next, add the eggs one at a time, each with a sprinkling of flour to avoid curdling. Stir in the orange zest and flour then slowly add the orange juice until you have a smooth batter.

Bake for 45 to 50 minutes or until a toothpick come out clean. If the top starts to brown too quickly loosely cover with buttered foil.

Allow to cool then carefully remove from the tin and discard the parchment. Place on a plate.

For the icing, sift the sugar into a clean bowl and stir in small amounts of juice until you have a spreadable consistency. Spread evenly over the top and let it drizzle down the side and leave to set.

Each portion provides 6g protein and 560kcals.

nutrient	thumbs-up score
vitamin A (total retinol equivalents)	👍👍
vitamin C	👍
calcium	👍
iodine	👍
phosphorus	👍
sodium	👍

Gingerbread waffles

Yield: 8 as a snack (easy to prepare)

Gingerbread isn't just for Christmas! These little beauties are great anytime of year.

2 eggs, at room temperature & separated
½ cup firmly packed dark brown sugar
½ cup dark treacle (molasses)
¼ cup unsalted butter, melted
2 cups sifted all-purpose flour
¼ tsp salt
2 tsp ground ginger
1½ tsp baking powder
2 tsp cinnamon
¼ tsp ground cloves
⅔ cup milk
vegetable oil for brushing the waffle iron

Beat together the egg yolks and brown sugar until the mixture is thick and pale then beat in the treacle and butter. In another bowl, sift together the flour, ginger, baking powder, salt, cloves and 1 teaspoon of the cinnamon. Add the dry mixture alternatively with the milk to the molasses mixture to make a smooth batter.

In a clean bowl and using an electric mixer, beat the egg whites until they hold soft peaks then fold them gently into the batter making sure you keep in as much air as possible.

Heat a well-seasoned or non-stick waffle iron until to hot, brush lightly with a bit of oil and spoon on just enough batter to thickly coat the iron. Cook the waffles according to the manufacturer's instructions or if using a stovetop iron cook until the surface is covered with 'popped bubbles' and the waffles lift easily, flip and cook through on the other side. They should be light and cakey. Top with ice cream or whipping cream.

Each waffle provides 5g protein and 230 kcals.

nutrient	thumbs-up score
vitamin B12	👍
phosphorus	👍

Chocolate banana muffins

Yields 1 loaf (easy to prepare)

I've shown this recipe as mini-muffins instead of a big loaf. Its delicious either way but lends itself to little and often tidbits.

250 g plain flour
25 g cocoa powder
1 tsp baking powder
¼ tsp bicarbonate of soda
a pinch of salt
200 g golden caster sugar (or regular)
2 very ripe bananas, peeled & mashed
2 large eggs, beaten
125 g butter, melted
100 g chocolate chips, chopped
50 g walnuts, chopped (optional)

Preheat oven to 170ºCf and grease and line a 23 cm loaf tin. Sift together the flour, cocoa, baking powder, bicarbonate of soda, salt and sugar. In a separate bowl beat the eggs with the melted butter then fold in the banana. Stir in the flour mixture until the batter is just combined then add the chocolate pieces and walnuts. Pour into the loaf tin and bake for 50 to 60 minutes until a toothpick comes out clean. Remove from the oven and cool for 10 minutes then remove from the tin.

If you prefer, pour the batter into cupcake liners and reduce the baking time and if you fancy the mini-muffins, pouring the batter into a piping bag will make it easier to fill the small liners and the baking time is only about 10 to 12 minutes – you have to keep an eye on them!

Each portion provides 7g protein and 480kcals.

nutrient	thumbs-up score
phosphorus	👍
copper	👍
vitamin B12	👍
vitamin A (total retinol equivalents)	nearly 👍
magnesium	nearly 👍

Vegetables & side dishes

The virtue of vegetables

Veg out!

It goes without saying that a healthy diet includes a wide range of vegetables. We can also safely say that vegetarian and vegan diets, when carefully considered and managed during treatment, are also a healthy lifestyle choice. It's worth it to occasionally remind ourselves why. Fruits and vegetables are often grouped together in healthy eating guidance but here we're just going to focus on the wonderful diversity and nutrition in vegetables.

Eating a plant-based diet can help to protect against certain types of cancers and reduce risk of heart disease, obesity and Type-2 diabetes and vegetables are right up there as some of our favourite foods. Rich in potassium they can also help lower blood pressure and may even lower the risk of developing kidney stones. They are almost always low in fat and calories and generally are some of the best sources of the nutrients we need.

Fibre, folate, vitamin A, C and iron – all these essential nutrients that keep our hair, skin, eyes, bones and muscles in good shape are all there.

What's so wonderful is that vegetables are so abundant, inexpensive and versatile. I think it's great that mainstream dining and cookery now includes vegetarian and vegan dishes as an integral part rather than a special diet or afterthought.

Take care though, when you're about to embark upon your treatment no matter how healthy it is, it's not the right time to make radical changes to what you eat. Gradual changes toward plant-based eating is a good goal to have and your specialist team can help you with tailor-made guidance to help you achieve this.

Get moving

Be your personal best

If you were a runner, a gym enthusiast or any other kind of athlete or sportsperson before diagnosis, keep on keeping on – but there are caveats.

Tell your medical team what you're used to doing and ask their advice, (a specialist physio will be a good source of information). For now, you will need to get used to a new normal, as treatment and surgery take their toll. Be kind to yourself. If you're having a tough day, go easy. As always, stop if you feel sharp pain – don't push through.

That doesn't mean not setting goals. The World Cancer Research Fund UK suggests that, as your fitness improves, you should aim for 60 minutes or more of moderate, or 30 minutes or more of vigorous, physical activity every day.

So go for a new personal best. It might be a charity walk or run, mastering Pilates, taking up a new sport or teaching others. Challenge yourself. People who train through treatment and beyond swear by the benefits and are rightly proud of every achievement.

Looking good feels better

I'm just going to veg today

The vitamin B family including biotin, folate, thiamin (vitamin B1) and pantothenic acid (vitamin B5), are critical for repairing and maintaining a healthy scalp and hair and some of the richest sources come from vegetables.

We all deserve a wee pat on the back and should reward ourselves when we triumph over the challenges that test us.

I can't resist a piece of good chocolate and maybe a tipple of something fizzy. I think we should reward our hair and skin as well, so a spinach and watercress salad with fresh mushrooms would be just the treat.

Potato dauphinoise

Serves 4 (medium difficulty to prepare)

These potatoes are so rich and creamy and the aroma is like no other. If waking up the tastebuds was an Olympic sport, potatoes dauphinoise would take the gold medal!

7 to 8 waxy potatoes
3 garlic cloves, crushed
a dash of sriracha*
splash of olive oil
200 ml double cream
200 g crème fraîche
120 g Parmesan cheese, finely grated
300 ml milk
salt & white pepper

Preheat oven to 170°Cf. Peel the potatoes and slice finely with a mandolin or sharp knife.

In a lightly oiled, deep frying pan, heat the garlic and sriracha. Pour in a little cream, then layers of potatoes separated by equal amounts of double cream, crème fraîche and sprinkles of Parmesan and pepper. Fill the pan with milk and simmer for about 15 minutes until really starchy.

Transfer the potatoes to a buttered baking dish. Add more milk if the mixture seems a bit dry. Cover with Parmesan, salt and pepper. Bake for 1 to 1½ hours until the potatoes are soft to a sharp knife and the surface is nicely golden.

Leave for at least 20 minutes before serving.

This dish can be prepared the night before and then cut with a scone cutter to make elegant little towers.

Each portion provides 18g protein and 690kcals.

* see *The basic & extras,* page 285

nutrient	thumbs-up score
vitamin A (total retinol equivalents)	>👍👍👍👍
vitamin B6	>👍👍👍👍
vitamin B12	>👍👍👍👍
calcium	👍👍👍
phosphorous	👍👍👍
iodine	👍👍
sodium	👍👍
chloride	👍👍
vitamin C	👍
riboflavin	👍
copper	👍
potassium	👍
protein	👍
zinc	👍

Potato rosti ⚖

Serves 4 (easy to prepare)

Rosti is a knockout served with just about anything. It's an easy at home option to triple cooked chips. Ooh, I just love it.

1 onion, finely chopped
45 g butter
1 tsp olive oil
650 g waxy potatoes
salt & pepper

You need a 9 inch, non-stick frying pan for this.

Melt half the butter and oil in a pan over low heat. Cook the onions without colour and remove from the heat.

Peel and cut the potatoes into large, even chunks. Place in a large saucepan, fill with cold water and lightly salt. Bring to the boil and simmer for 5 minutes. They should still be firm. Drain, dry and allow to cool slightly then coarsely grate the potatoes. Gently stir in the onions and season to taste.

Heat the remaining butter with a tiny splash of oil over low heat and add the potatoes making a flat cake with a fork. Allow to cook for 15 minutes shaking the pan frequently so the potatoes do not stick. Continue until the bottom is a golden crust.

To flip the rosti, place a plate larger than the pan on top and flip them together. Quickly slide the rosti, uncooked side down back into the pan and cook for another 15 minutes or until this side also has a golden crust. Season to taste and cut into wedges to serve.

Each portion provides 4g protein and 220kcals.

nutrient	thumbs-up score
vitamin B6	👍👍👍
vitamin C	👍
vitamin D	👍
sodium	👍
chloride	👍

Potato purée ⚖

Serves 4 (easy to prepare)

Potato purée is the king of all comfort foods!

700 g floury potatoes
100 ml milk
60 g butter
salt & white pepper
nutmeg, freshly grated

nutrient	thumbs-up score
chloride	👍👍
sodium	👍
vitamin A (total retinol equivalents)	👍
vitamin B6	👍
vitamin B12	👍
vitamin C	👍
folate	👍
thiamin	👍
potassium	👍

Peel the potatoes and chop into 3 inch chunks. Place in a pot of cold salted water then boil until potatoes are fully cooked through. A knife or fork should pass easily through but the flesh should not fall apart.

Fully drain the potatoes then transfer to a bowl. Pass the potatoes through a ricer back into the original pot. Next, whisk in the butter and milk until the consistency is smooth and creamy but with body. Season to taste and grate in a bit of nutmeg.

Helpful potato hints – if you can buy them from a market with dirt still on do so. It will ensure that the potatoes have not been refrigerated so no nutritional value is lost. If you don't have a ricer, break the potatoes up with a masher then finish them with a strong whisk and good-old-fashioned elbow grease. Finally, use the potato water for your sauces and gravies to keep the water-soluble nutrients.

Each portion provides 5g protein and 260kcals.

Swede & potato mash ⚖

Serves 4 (easy to prepare)

This is a simple way to add a bit of variety, colour and stronger flavour to ordinary mash. For added nutritional value, whip in an egg. It's great with lamb.

350 g floury potatoes
350 g swede
120 ml milk
50 g butter
white pepper

Peel and cut equal amounts of potato and swede. Boil until soft, then pass through a ricer for a smooth purée or mash for a courser texture. Add milk, butter and white pepper to taste.

Each portion provides 3g protein and 150kcals.

nutrient	thumbs-up score
vitamin B6	>👍👍👍👍
vitamin C	👍👍
vitamin A (total retinol equivalents)	👍
vitamin B12	👍

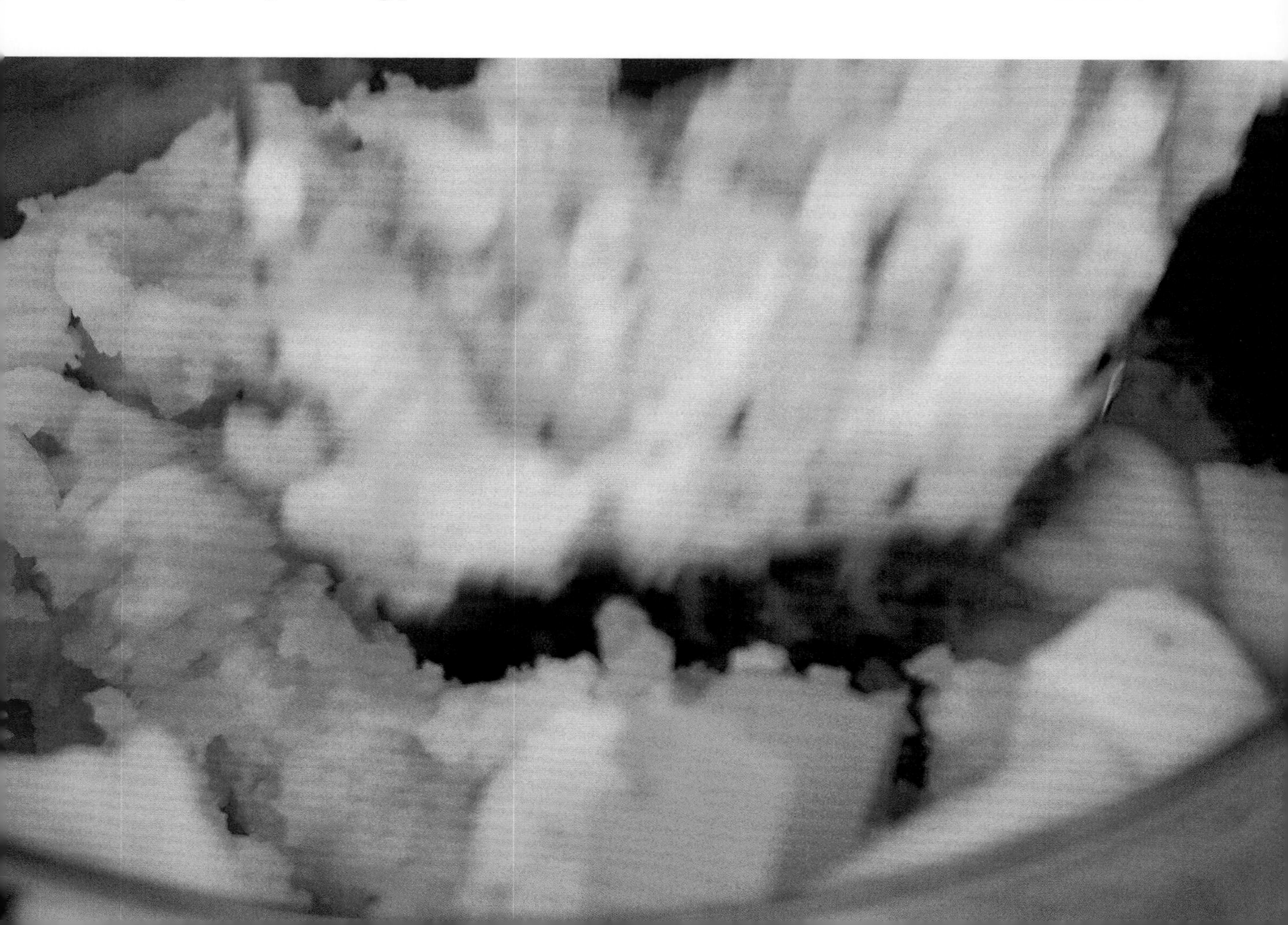

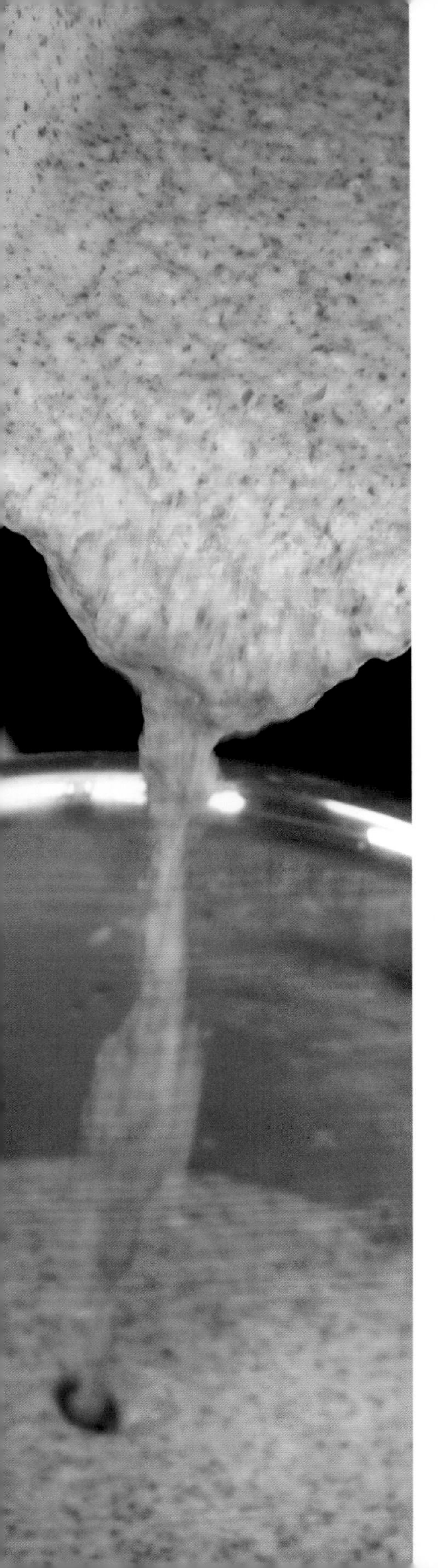

Broccoli purée ⚖

Serve as a side dish, (easy to prepare)

I think this is a perfect accompaniment to salmon in flavour texture and colour.

800 g broccoli florets
1 very small garlic clove, finely chopped
100 ml olive oil
¼ tsp white pepper
salt & pepper

Cook the broccoli florets in boiling water until they are fully cooked but not soggy. You should be able to pierce them with a knife. Drain them well and transfer to a bowl. Add the garlic, oil, white pepper and purée with a hand mixer. Season to taste. Gently reheat before serving.

Each portion provides 9g protein and 70kcals.

nutrient	thumbs-up score
vitamin C	>👍👍👍👍
folate	👍👍
vitamin A (total retinol equivalents)	👍
vitamin B6	👍
fibre (non-starch polysaccaride)	👍
phosphorus	👍
potassium	👍
sodium	👍
chloride	👍

Brittany courgette ⚖

Serve as a side dish (easy to prepare)

This is just a lovely way to serve courgette. It's a nice accompaniment to roast chicken or game.

5 courgettes, diced into fine cubes
a splash of olive oil
3 garlic cloves, puréed
a dash of sriracha*
salt & pepper

Warm the garlic and sriracha in a deep oiled saucepan. Add the courgette and stew on very low heat for about an hour. Stir lightly with a wooden spoon so the cubes do not lose their shape. Season to taste and serve as a side dish.

Each portion provides 4g protein and 37kcals.

* see *The basic & extras,* page 285

nutrient	thumbs-up score
vitamin C	👍👍
vitamin A (total retinol equivalents)	👍
vitamin B6	👍
folate	👍
potassium	👍
sodium	👍
chloride	👍
iodine	👍
riboflavin	👍

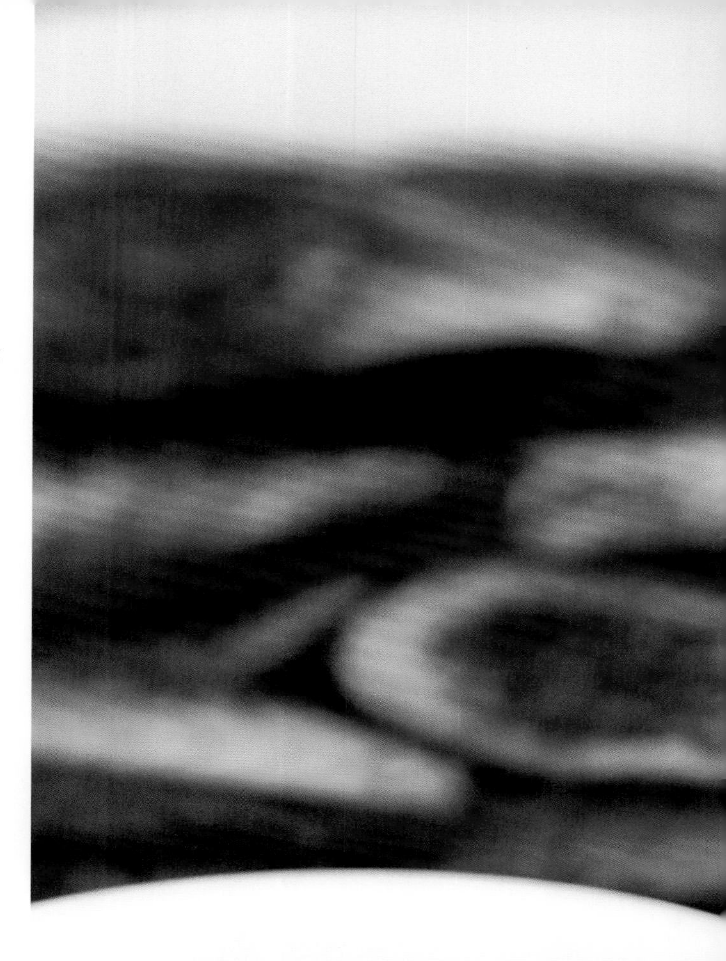

Refried pinto beans ⚖

Serves 4 to 6 as a side (medium difficulty to prepare)

Unsurprisingly these are best served with chicken enchiladas, tacos, salsa and maybe a margarita. They are soft, mild and so easy to eat and digest.

200 g dried pinto beans,
(or half pinto & half black beans)
2 bay leaves
1 whole garlic bulb
175 ml olive oil
1 tin chopped tomatoes
3 tsp salt
1 cup spring onions, chopped

Rinse the beans thoroughly. Discard any that are shriveled. Place in a pan with 8 cups water. Do not add any salt as this can dry out the beans. Add the bay leaves and bring to the boil, then lower the heat and simmer for 2 hours or until the beans are soft. Add more boiling water as required to keep the level up and stir occasionally.

Preheat oven to 200°Cf. Brush the garlic bulb with oil and roast for 15 to 20 minutes. The flesh should squeeze easily from the husks. Remove any excess water from the beans and add the rest of the oil, tomatoes, garlic and salt. Allow to simmer for another 1½ hours. Don't rush this, as you want the flavours to intensify and the texture to soften. When soft, lightly mash and season to taste. Sprinkle over the chopped spring onion and serve warm.

Each portion provides 8g protein and 110kcals.

nutrient	thumbs-up score
sodium	👍👍👍👍
chloride	👍👍👍👍
folate	👍👍
vitamin B6	
vitamin C	👍👍
thiamin	👍
copper	👍
fibre (non-starch polysaccaride)	👍
iron	👍
phosphorus	👍
potassium	👍

French bean & onion ring casserole

Serves 4 to 6 as a side (medium difficulty to prepare)

This is vintage American comfort food at its finest. It never seems to grow tired. It's so morish so no wonder!

900 g French beans, trimmed
50 g butter
a splash of olive oil
1 onion, chopped
225 g button or small cup mushrooms, sliced
1 garlic clove, finely chopped
leaves of 2 thyme sprigs
2 tbsp flour
150 ml white wine
250 ml vegetable stock
120 ml double cream
salt & pepper
225 g Gruyère, finely grated
a handful of fine breadcrumbs
½ cup fried onion rings*, coarsely chopped

Boil enough salted water to blanche the beans. When they have softened plunge them in cold water, drain and set aside to dry.

Melt a knob of butter on medium-low heat in a lightly oiled pan and cook the onions without colour. Add the mushrooms, garlic and thyme and sauté for 10 minutes allowing the mushrooms to slightly caramelise, then sprinkle on flour and mix. Stir in the wine, stock and cream and allow the mixture to thicken. Add extra stock if it gets too thick. Finally stir in the beans and cheese.

Preheat oven to 170°Cf. Transfer the mixture to a greased casserole, top with onion ring pieces and sprinkle with breadcrumbs. Bake until the casserole is bubbling and golden brown on top. Serve hot.

Each portion provides 19g protein and 565kcals.

**Use store-bought frozen onion rings and follow the package instructions to cook them so they are crispy but not burned. You can also use dry tinned ones straight from the package.*

nutrient	thumbs-up score
vitamin A (total retinol equivalents)	👍👍👍👍
calcium	👍👍👍👍
vitamin B12	👍👍👍
phosphorus	👍👍👍
sodium	👍👍👍
chloride	👍👍👍
copper	👍👍
vitamin B6	👍
folate	👍
riboflavin	👍
protein	👍

Globe artichokes with lemon mayo

Serves 4, (easy to prepare)

These are simply my favourite. It takes a while to work through all the leaves and getting to the heart is a bit of a faff but it's worth it. Go the extra mile and make fresh mayonnaise.

4 large globe artichokes
400 g lemon mayonnaise* (about ¼ cup per serving)
1 lemon, cut into 4 wedges

Put a pan of water large enough to hold and submerge the artichokes on high heat and bring to the boil.

Top and tail the artichokes by cutting about 1 inch off the top of the leaves and cut the stem off just into the leaves. Remove any small and very tough leaves from the bottom. Fully submerge the artichokes in the water, turn down the heat and allow to simmer for 30 to 40 minutes. Check them frequently as the time will vary due to size. They are done when the base is soft but firm and a knife will slide into the heart at the bottom. Don't overcook. Drain the artichokes on paper towel to remove excess moisture and cut away any loose leaves from the bottom.

Make the mayonnaise*. If using store-bought, squeeze in some lemon juice to give it some zing.

Serve with mayonnaise on the side and a bowl for discarding the leaves. Tear off each leaf and dip in the mayonnaise, eating only the tender inside flesh. When you get to the thin leaves and 'hair' inside, use a knife or spoon to lift this away and discard leaving the lovely round heart as your reward.

Each portion provides 5g protein and 800kcals.

*see *The basics & extras*, page 285

nutrient	thumbs-up score
vitamin B12	👍👍👍
folate	👍👍👍
sodium	👍
chloride	👍

Roasted okra ⚖

Serves 4 (easy to prepare)

I included these because many people look at these beauties at the market but don't know a basic preparation and they are a perfect curry and creole partner. So here's a really simple method.

20 okra
2 Italian tomatoes, de-seeded & cut into fine petals
a drizzle of olive oil
salt & pepper

Preheat oven to 170°Cf. Line a baking pan with tin foil. Trim off the tops and place the okra and tomatoes petals flat on the tray. Drizzle with oil and season. Roast for 12 to 15 minutes or until the okra is cooked through. That's it! Serve hot.

Simply roasting the vegetables keeps them from becoming too gummy as well.

Each portion provides 2g protein and 25kcals.

nutrient	thumbs-up score
vitamin C	👍
sodium	👍
chloride	👍

Creamy cheesy leeks ⚖

Serves 4 as a side (medium difficulty to prepare)

Leeks are so full of flavour and are true nutritional best friends. They are great with roast chicken or turkey.

2 leeks, white only, sliced
2 shallots, peeled & finely chopped
a splash of olive oil
40 g butter
2 sprigs of thyme
75 ml white wine
120 ml double cream
salt & pepper
50 g Gruyère cheese, finely grated

Melt the butter in a lightly oiled pan. Add the leeks, shallots and thyme and cook without colour. Lightly season and add white wine. Sauté on low heat for another 2 minutes then add the cream and continue to cook until the mixture is thickening but not dry.

Preheat oven to 170°Cf. Transfer the leeks into a greased casserole, cover with cheese and bake until the cheese is melted and light golden. Serve hot.

Each portion provides 4g protein and 290kcals.

nutrient	thumbs-up score
vitamin A (total retinol equivalents)	👍👍
sodium	👍👍
chloride	👍👍
vitamin B12	👍
calcium	👍

Sauté of Asian vegetables ⚖

serves 4 (easy to prepare)

These are such fresh and flavourful vegetables. The stir-fry keeps all the water-soluble vitamins in. They're a perfect accompliment to fish like tuna. Mmm!

1 tbsp ground nut oil
1 garlic clove, puréed
a dash of sriracha*
150 g baby corn
1 Thai green pepper, chopped
150 g baby pak choi, chopped
150 g shiitake mushrooms
1 onion, quartered
1 tin water chestnuts, drained & rinsed (optional)
2 celery stalks, cut into 2 inch sticks
150 g small whole green onions
1 tbsp tamari soy sauce
3 cm fresh ginger, peeled & finely julienned
1 tbsp mirin

Warm the garlic and oil in a wok. Add the sriracha and vegetables and stir-fry for a minute or two, then add the soy sauce, ginger and mirin. Simmer until just cooked through. Serve hot in a big bowl with the juices.

Each portion provides 3g protein and 95kcals.

* see *The basics & extras,* page 285

nutrient	thumbs-up score
vitamin C	👍👍
sodium	👍👍
chloride	👍👍
vitamin B6	👍

Jasmine coconut rice ⚖

Serves 4 (easy to prepare)

This sticky, slightly sweet rice is lovely with fish and curries.

1 cup jasmine rice
1 cup water
1 cup coconut milk

Cook the rice in the water with coconut milk. Bring just to the boil then turn heat to low and allow the rice to absorb the liquid. When nearly cooked turn the heat off and be careful not to burn the bottom of the pan. Serve hot.

Each portion provides 5g protein and 250kcals.

nutrient	thumbs-up score
copper	👍
phosphorus	👍

Stuffed globe courgette ⚖

Serves 4 (medium difficulty to prepare)

This is a small portion veggie take on stuffed marrow. If you can't get globe courgette use regular ones by splitting them down the middle like mini marrows. They're fab.

4 globe courgette
a splash of olive oil
1 onion, finely chopped
2 large shallots, finely chopped
4 Italian tomatoes, de-seeded & finely chopped
1 garlic clove, puréed
2 tbsp flat parsley, chopped
leaves from 1 sprig of thyme
50 ml white wine
40 g Parmesan cheese, grated
salt & pepper

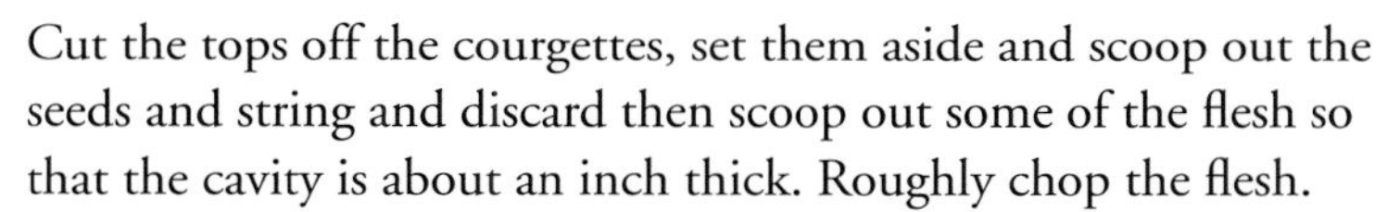

Cut the tops off the courgettes, set them aside and scoop out the seeds and string and discard then scoop out some of the flesh so that the cavity is about an inch thick. Roughly chop the flesh.

In an oiled pan, cook the onions and shallots without colour then add the courgette flesh, tomatoes, garlic, parsley, thyme and wine. Allow to cook until excess moisture has evaporated, stirring gently from time to time. Season to taste.

Preheat the oven to 170°Cf. When ready to stuff and bake, mix in most of the cheese, leaving a little for the top of each. Stuff the cavities to slightly over full then sprinkle on the remaining cheese and replace the tops as little hats. The cheese will act as glue to keep them in place. Place on a baking tray in the oven for about 30 to 40 minutes. You know they are done when you give them a light squeeze and they give but are still firm.

Each portion provides 7g protein and 100kcals.

nutrient	thumbs-up score
vitamin C	👍👍
vitamin A (total retinol equivalents)	👍
vitamin B6	👍
vitamin B12	👍
folate	👍
calcium	👍
phosphorus	👍
potassium	👍
sodium	👍
chloride	

'Simply the best' Yorkshire pudding ⚖

Serves 6 (medium difficulty to prepare)

I've included this recipe because it is the most reliable one I've come across and I love them with just about every dinner.

140 g plain flour
4 eggs
200 ml milk
salt & pepper
a splash of sunflower oil for cooking

Preheat oven to 230°Cf. Drizzle some oil into 6 to 8 non-stick muffin tins or a 22 cm square cake tin. Place them in the oven to heat.

Place the flour in a clean bowl, add the eggs and whisk until smooth. Whisk in the milk and a bit of seasoning until completely smooth.

Remove the hot tins from the oven and pour in equal amounts for the individual muffins or all for the cake tin. Place them back in the hot oven for 20 to 25 minutes. They should be nicely puffed up and browned.
Serve immediately.

These little chappies will also freeze for up to a month.
Just take out and re-heat.

Each portion provides 7g protein and 160kcals.

nutrient	thumbs-up score
vitamin B12	👍👍👍👍
riboflavin	👍
iodine	👍
phosphorous	👍

Smoked haddock with pea & baby leek risotto

see page 214

Main dishes

Pasta & risotto

Smoked wild salmon & caviar fettuccini

Old-fashioned tuna casserole

Stuffed marrow with tagliatelle

Dijon & four cheese macaroni

Beetroot risotto

Turkey rigatoni

Smoked haddock with pea & baby leek risotto

Poultry & game

Coq au vin

Chicken, leek & mushroom chasseur

Turkey bubble & squeak

Crispy duck pancakes

Fish & shellfish

Trout fillets with tomatoes, ginger & lemongrass

Sri Lankan wet fish curry

Tuna, courgette & pepper frittata

Fish pie

Lemon sole fillet tacos & salsa

Baked sea bass with cep

Grilled sardine with wasabi butter

Beef, pork & lamb

Beef bourguignon

Cabbage rolls

Escalope of pork with juniper & Marsala

Simon's pie

Welsh cawl

Supper time
Meals & full portions

Treatment can radically affect the way you perceive food and one common challenge with loss of appetite and the desire to eat is portion size, particularly on or just after treatment days. Even with main dishes the 'little and often' rule is helpful. Sharing meals with family, friends and loved ones is a positive antidote and soothing for the soul.

Try to think of foods that are easy to serve in small portions. Choose lean and tender cuts of meat and vegetables that are naturally easy to digest and trust your body to tell you what it needs. Most of all be patient with yourself.

Not all meals need to be prepared in 15 minutes and consumed in five.

When my husband Simon was in treatment we always had simple dishes before, on and just following treatment days. Things like Simon's Pie, easy egg dishes or even just beans on toast. I thought through dishes that were quick to prepare in advance and it made coming home welcoming.

Save your favourite foods for the top of your cycle so you associate the things you enjoy most with feeling stronger and well. It's a powerful way to keep food on your side.

Get moving

Find your balance

Chemotherapy can affect your balance, which deteriorates with age in any case. It's important to work on this, as poor balance, (combined with weak muscles), can cause falls and a loss of confidence, even if you don't break bones. As some forms of chemo and accompanying steroids can cause loss of bone density, this can be a real possibility.

Something as simple as standing on one leg while waiting for the kettle to boil or brushing your teeth can really help. Swap legs when you get wobbly – or half way through if your balance is good – and make sure you have something to grab onto if you need it. There are more ideas for improving your balance on page 319.

Looking good feels better

Something for a rainy day

It's human nature to use the weather as a measure of how we feel. It's easier to feel uplifted when basking in warm sunshine and equally convenient to feel down on a gloomy day.

Just like the weather, you can't predict how you're going to respond to treatment and the impact of losing your hair. Everybody's different but one thing is almost certain, there will be stormy times ahead.

A dull day is a perfect time to get together with a friend that brightens your spirits to spoil yourselves with a bit of TLC.

It doesn't matter what it is; maybe a pedicure, massage or that wig fitting you've been putting off. That way, when the sun returns, you're looking good and hopefully feeling even better.

One helpful hint – chemo can dramatically dry your eyes causing your tear ducts to over compensate. Try not to rub your eyes and avoid direct contact with your hands as you'll be more susceptible to infection and ask your doctor about artificial tears or eye drops to reduce the irritation.

Smoked wild salmon & caviar fettuccini

Serves, 4 (easy to prepare)

This is elegant and simple pasta that smiles. It always seems to say, 'I'm special.' The textures are simply wonderful.

a knob of butter
1 garlic clove, finely sliced
1 shallot, finely chopped
85 ml white wine
175 ml whipping cream
225 g fettuccini*
1 carrot, 1 stick celery & ½ leek, julienned
100 g smoked wild salmon
100 g Parmesan cheese, grated
a pinch of nutmeg
a pinch of cayenne pepper
salt & pepper
a jar of lumpfish caviar

Boil the pasta in salted water to al dente. Strain into a bowl of ice water and set aside. Next sauté the garlic and shallots in butter. Cook without colour for 2 minutes then add the white wine and reduce by two-thirds. Add the cream and boil for 2 minutes. When ready to serve add the fettuccine, julienne of vegetables and salmon to the sauce, combine and turn the heat down low.

Just before serving, turn the heat back up, bring to the boil, season to taste and add half the Parmesan cheese, the nutmeg and cayenne pepper.

Garnish with a dollop of caviar and the rest of the Parmesan.

Each portion provides 25g protein and 495kcals.

*see *The basics & extras*, page 285

nutrient	thumbs-up score
vitamin A (total retinol equivalents)	>👍👍👍👍
vitamin B12	>👍👍👍👍
sodium	👍👍👍👍
chloride	👍👍👍👍
vitamin B6	👍👍👍
phosphorus	👍👍👍
calcium	👍👍
copper	👍👍
protein	👍👍
riboflavin	👍
iodine	👍
selenium	👍
zinc	👍

Old-fashioned tuna casserole

Serves 4 (easy to prepare)

This all-American classic is famous for its ease and economy. It's a nutritious powerhouse and a fast way to feed the family. It's also famous for being a dish that you would bring to an ailing friend.

400 g dry pasta (orecchiette is great)
370 g flaked tuna, 2 tins, drained, rinsed & dried
500 ml condensed cream of mushroom soup, 2 tins
a knob of butter
1 medium onion, finely chopped
6 medium cup mushrooms, sliced
½ green pepper, finely chopped (optional)
200 g petit pois
350 g Cheddar, grated
225 g lightly salted crisps

Preheat oven to 170°Cf. Boil the noodles in salted water until fully cooked then drain, rinse and set aside. Next sauté the onion, mushrooms and pepper in butter until soft.

In a large bowl add the soup, tuna, sautéed vegetables, peas and noodles and mix. Place these in a deep casserole and cover with cheese and top with crisps.

Bake for about 20 minutes, until hot and golden on top and serve.

Each portion provides 67g protein and 1360kcals.

nutrient	thumbs-up score
vitamin B6	>👍👍👍👍
vitamin B12	>👍👍👍👍
calcium	>👍👍👍👍
protein	>👍👍👍👍
phosphorus	>👍👍👍👍
selenium	>👍👍👍👍
sodium	>👍👍👍👍
chloride	>👍👍👍👍
vitamin C	👍👍👍👍
niacin	👍👍👍👍
vitamin A total retinol equivalents)	👍👍👍
copper	👍👍👍
zinc	👍👍👍
folate	👍👍
riboflavin	👍👍
fibre (non-starch polysaccaride)	👍👍
iron	👍👍
magnesium	👍👍
potassium	👍👍
vitamin D	👍
thiamin	👍
iodine	👍

Stuffed marrow with tagliatelle

Serves 6 (medium difficulty to prepare)

This wonderful family dish is easy to convert to a hearty vegetarian meal.

1 medium marrow
55 g butter
a drizzle of olive oil
2 to 3 garlic cloves, crushed
1 large carrot, finely chopped
1 stalk celery, finely chopped
1 medium onion, finely chopped
55 g minced pancetta
100 g minced lean beef
100 g minced lean pork
a dash of sriracha*
800 g chopped tomatoes, 2 tins
a glass of red wine (optional)
a little beef or chicken stock
3 tbsp tomato purée
a handful of dried Italian herbs
225 g dry tagliatelle
150 g Parmesan cheese, grated
salt & pepper

Cut the marrow in half and scoop out the seeds and string and discard then scoop out some of the flesh so that the cavity is about 3 cm thick. Roughly chop the flesh to add to the ragu.

For the ragu, heat the oil and butter in a large pan, add a garlic clove, carrot, celery and onion and cook without colour on low heat. Add the chopped tomatoes and half the herbs and cook for another 30 minutes seasoning to taste. Liquidise the mixture.

In a lightly oiled pan, brown the pancetta and minced meats with the remaining garlic and sriracha. Add herbs and seasoning using a wooden spoon to break up evenly. When browned, add the wine and bubble for a few minutes to allow the alcohol to evaporate. Stir in a little stock to prevent the mixture sticking. Next add tomato purée and dilute with a bit more stock as required. Place the tomato mixture and meat in a pot and simmer for approximately 1½ hours, adding stock as the sauce reduces. Season to taste.

Preheat oven to 170°Cf. When ready to stuff and bake, mix in most of the cheese, leaving a little for the top of each. Stuff the cavity to slightly over full then sprinkle on the remaining cheese and replace the top. Place on a baking tray in the oven for about 1 hour. You know it's done when you give it a light squeeze and it gives but remains firm.

Serve with cooked tagliatelle.

Each portion provides 27g protein and 480kcals.

* see *The basics & extras*, page 285

nutrient	thumbs-up score
vitamin A (total retinol equivalents)	>👍👍👍👍
vitamin B12	👍👍👍
phosphorus	👍👍👍
sodium	👍👍👍
chloride	👍👍
vitamin C	👍👍
calcium	👍👍
protein	👍👍
vitamin B6	👍
niacin	👍
thiamin	👍
folate	👍
copper	👍
fibre (as non-starch polysaccharide)	👍
iron	👍
magnesium	👍
potassium	👍
zinc	👍

Dijon & four cheese macaroni

Serves 4 (easy to prepare)

Whenever I can't think of what to prepare I revert to 'mac 'n cheese'. There really is nothing quite like it. The beauty of this dish is that you can use any cheese you have handy and it will still be delicious.

6 to 8 smoked bacon rashers (optional)
250 g macaroni
a knob of butter
1 tbsp flour, sifted
300 ml milk
2 tbsp Dijon mustard
100 g mature Cheddar cheese, grated
50 g Emmenthal cheese, grated
1 tbsp cream cheese
50 g Parmesan cheese, grated
⅛ cup breadcrumbs
salt & pepper

Preheat oven to 170°Cf. Fry or grill the bacon until crisp then pat dry and break into pieces. Cook the macaroni thoroughly; you do not want the pasta al dente as it will absorb the cheese sauce when baking.

To make the cheese sauce, start by making a roux* and gently warming the milk. Gradually add the warmed milk to the roux, stirring constantly. Lightly season and add the mustard. Cook but don't boil for about 2 minutes. Never stop stirring!

Gradually add the cream cheese, Cheddar and Emmenthal in small amounts melting thoroughly. Keep tasting as the sauce thickens adjust seasoning as required.
Leave on a gentle boil for several minutes until reduced by one third.
Finally, stir in a knob of butter.

Butter a casserole dish. Add the bacon and cooked macaroni. Cover with the cheese sauce then sprinkle with Parmesan and breadcrumbs.

Bake for 20 minutes or until the top is golden brown.

Each portion provides 39g protein and 740kcals.

*see *The basics & extras*, page 285

nutrient	thumbs-up score
vitamin B6	>👍👍👍👍
sodium	👍👍👍
chloride	👍👍👍
vitamin C	👍
thiamin	👍
calcium	👍
copper	👍
fibre (as non-starch polysaccharide)	👍
folate	👍
iron	👍
phosphorus	👍
protein	👍

Beetroot risotto

Serves 4 (medium difficulty to prepare)

The colour of this is marvellous. This is great on its own or as a partner with fish and shellfish.

500 g beetroot
2 tbsp olive oil
1 onion, finely diced
1 garlic clove, puréed
250 g risotto rice
150 ml white wine (optional)
700 ml vegetable stock (or more if not using wine)
a few shavings of Parmesan cheese
a few sprigs of fresh dill
crème fraîche
salt & pepper

Preheat oven to 170°Cf. Cut the beetroot into quarters, lightly brush with oil and place in the oven on a baking tray. Roast it for 1 hour or until soft. Set it aside to cool then remove the skin. Purée half with a hand blender and mix with the stock then finely dice the other half.

Coat the bottom of a pan with oil, melt the butter then add the onion and garlic and cook without colour on medium heat then add the rice and stir to coat the grains and allow to warm. Pour in the wine, (or 150 ml of stock) and simmer for 1 minute.

Over medium low heat start adding the rest of the stock to the rice a ladle at a time allowing the rice to absorb and checking the seasoning as you go. When the rice is al dente stir in the beetroot and a bit of the cheese. Season to taste. Garnish with a dollop of crème fraîche, a few shavings of Parmesan cheese and a sprinkle of dill. Serve immediately.

Each portion provides 10g protein and 360kcals.

nutrient	thumbs-up score
sodium	👍👍👍
chloride	👍👍
folate	👍👍
phosphorus	👍👍
vitamin B6	👍
thiamin	👍
calcium	👍
copper	👍
fibre (non-starch polysaccaride)	👍
potassium	👍
protein	👍
zinc	👍

Turkey rigatoni

Serves 4 (easy to medium difficulty to prepare)

Turkey gets a bit of a bum rap except at Christmas. It shouldn't. It's one of the healthiest and most nutritious meats and it's readily available.

a splash of olive oil
275 g minced turkey
150 g smoked turkey or bacon rashers, chopped
2 garlic cloves, smashed
120 ml white wine
1 onion, finely chopped
2 carrots, finely diced
50 ml tomato purée
300 ml chicken stock
a handful of mixed herbs
225 g dry rigatoni
50 g Parmesan cheese, grated
salt & pepper

Warm oil in a large pan, add one clove of garlic and cook without colour. Add the turkey mince breaking it into a fine texture with a wooden spoon and cook until browned. Remove from the pan.

Next add the rashers, onions, carrots and white wine to the pan and allow to simmer for 5 minutes until the vegetables are cooked. Place the mixture in a bowl and using a hand blender whiz into a rough purée and return to the pan with the mince.

Add the tomato purée and chicken stock to the mixture and season with herbs and salt & pepper to taste. Allow the turkey ragu to simmer on low heat for at least 30 to 45 minutes to allow the flavours to blend adding additional stock if needed. Continue to check seasoning.

Preheat oven to 160°Cf. Boil the rigatoni in salted water to al dente, drain thoroughly and mix with the ragu. Transfer to a deep casserole, sprinkle generously with cheese and pop in the oven for 20 to 30 minutes.

Serve hot with crusty garlic bread.

Each portion provides 35g protein and 480kcals.

nutrient	thumbs-up score
vitamin A (total retinol equivalents)	>👍👍👍👍
vitamin B12	>👍👍👍👍
phosphorus	👍👍👍👍
protein	👍👍👍👍
sodium	👍👍👍
chloride	👍👍
vitamin B6	👍👍
niacin	👍👍
riboflavin	👍
thiamin	👍
folate	👍
calcium	👍
copper	👍
fibre (non-starch polysaccharide)	👍
iron	👍
magnesium	👍
potassium	👍
selenium	👍
zinc	👍

Smoked haddock with pea & baby leek risotto

– see illustration on page 198

Serves 4 (medium difficulty to prepare)

This risotto is packed with flavour, texture and nutrition. It might look a bit fiddly but it's quite straight forward and what a result!

1 large shallot, finely chopped
1 small leek, white only finely sliced
1 bay leaf
a sprig of thyme
a splash of olive oil
a large knob of butter
225 g risotto rice
150 ml white wine (optional)
500 ml vegetable stock (or extra if not using wine)
a small handful of parsley, finely chopped
50 g petit pois
500 ml milk
1 fillet smoked haddock, undyed
juice of ½ lemon
20 g cream cheese
4 organic free-range eggs

Place the butter, shallot, leek, bay leaf and thyme in a pan and cook without colour. Stir in the rice and coat with the mixture and allow to warm for a minute. Discard the bay leaf and thyme stalk and pour in the wine. Start adding the stock a ladle at a time allowing the rice to absorb the moisture.

In the meantime, bring the milk to a simmer in another pan. Poach the haddock for 1 to 2 minutes. Lift from the milk, remove the skin, break into chunks and sprinkle with lemon juice.

When the risotto is al dente stir in the cream cheese, peas and parsley and gently fold in the haddock.

Poach the eggs*. To serve spoon risotto into a shallow bowl, top with egg. Serve immediately.

Each portion provides 22g protein and 490kcals.

*see *The basics & extras,* page 285

nutrient	thumbs-up score
vitamin B12	>👍👍👍👍
iodine	>👍👍👍👍
phosphorus	👍👍👍
vitamin B6	👍👍
riboflavin	👍👍
protein	👍👍
sodium	👍👍
chloride	👍
vitamin A total retinol equivalents)	👍
folate	👍
niacin	👍
thiamin	👍
calcium	👍
copper	👍
selenium	👍
zinc	👍

Trout fillets with tomatoes, ginger & lemongrass

Serves 4 (medium difficulty to prepare)

Surprisingly bold flavours for such a delicate fish. The colour is as bold as the flavour.

4 trout filets, skinned
100 g Italian tomatoes, de-seeded & finely diced
1 large shallot, finely chopped
1 garlic clove, finely chopped
1 small green chilli, finely chopped
1 stick fresh lemongrass, finely chopped
1 tsp fresh ginger, peeled & finely chopped
a pinch of saffron
24 capers, chopped
1 lime
4 tbsp olive oil
salt & pepper

Preheat oven to 170°Cf. Using tweezers, make sure all the fine bones are removed from the fillets. You can find them by gently rubbing your fingers over the flesh. Set in the refrigerator until ready to use.

Add together the tomatoes, shallot, garlic, chilli, lemongrass, ginger, saffron and capers in a bowl. Peel the lime removing all pith and cut into fine wedges removing the membranes as well. Add the lime segments to the mixture.

Season the fillets and place in a lightly oiled baking pan. Top with the tomato mixture then add a cup of water. Bake for 10 minutes. To serve drizzle with the cooking juices and a bit of olive oil.

Each portion provides 24g protein and 150kcals.

nutrient	thumbs-up score
vitamin B12	>👍👍👍👍
vitamin D	>👍👍👍👍
vitamin B6	👍👍
phosphorus	👍👍
protein	👍👍
vitamin C	👍
niacin	👍
sodium	👍
chloride	👍

Sri Lankan wet fish curry

Serves 4 (medium difficulty to prepare)

This is a delicious and traditional dish that ticks every box for colour, aroma and bags of flavour. It's perfect with the rice, poppadoms and mango chutney.

2 tsp yellow mustard seeds
a splash of vegetable oil
1 onion, chopped
4 garlic cloves, finely chopped
2 ½ cm piece of ginger, peeled & julienned
2 to 3 tbsp mild curry powder
2 tbsp desiccated coconut
1 tsp turmeric
1 tbsp chilli powder
1 tbsp tamarind paste
400 g tin coconut milk
4 green chillies. finely sliced
200 ml chicken stock
1 kg monkfish tail, or other firm white fish, cut into goujons
1 medium sweet potato, cut into 2 ½ cm pieces
a handful French beans, trimmed & blanched
a bunch of coriander, chopped
jasmine coconut rice to serve, (see page 193)

Cook the mustard seeds in some hot oil until they start to pop. Add the onion, garlic, ginger and curry powder, lower the heat and cook for 5 minutes. Next add the coconut, turmeric and chilli powder and cook for another 5 minutes. Add the tamarind sauce and cook for another 5 minutes, then add the coconut milk, chillies, sweet potato, green beans and chicken stock, stir well and simmer for about 30 minutes until the sweet potato is cooked through but still firm. Add the fish and simmer for another 15 minutes then garnish with coriander and serve with rice.

Each portion provides 48g protein and 560kcals with rice.

nutrient	thumbs-up score
vitamin B12	>👍👍👍👍
phosphorus	>👍👍👍👍
protein	👍👍👍
vitamin A (total retinol equivalents)	👍👍
chloride	👍👍
iron	👍👍
magnesium	👍👍
potassium	👍👍
sodium	👍
vitamin C	👍
riboflavin	👍
thiamin	
calcium	👍
copper	👍
fibre (as non-starch polysaccharide)	👍
zinc	👍

Tuna, courgette & pepper frittata

Serves 4 (easy to medium difficulty to prepare)

Fritatta is a simple way to pack an easy dish with nutrition. I've used fresh tuna but tinned works just as well.

15 ml sunflower oil
1 onion, chopped
1 courgette, thinly sliced
1 red bell pepper
4 eggs
30 ml milk
200 g tuna
2 tsp mixed herbs
50 g Emmenthal cheese, grated
salt & pepper

To start, rub the pepper with a fine coat of oil and put on a hot bbq or under a grill turning until the skin is evenly charred. Place in a plastic bag and allow to cool. Peel away and discard the charred skin, remove the seeds and slice the flesh into fine slices.

Next heat half the oil in a shallow pan and add the onion, courgette and pepper, stir frequently and cook without colour on low heat for about 5 minutes.

Chop the tuna into thin slices and add to the vegetables. Season to taste.

Preheat the grill to medium. Whisk the eggs, milk and herbs in a bowl then pour evenly over the tuna mixture occasionally pulling the sides into the middle to allow the uncooked mixture to run to the edges and continue to cook until the bottom is lightly golden.

Sprinkle the cheese onto the frittata and place under the grill and cook until the cheese has melted and the frittata is golden brown. Serve hot with a light salad and vinegrette.

Each portion provides 23g protein and 240kcals.

nutrient	thumbs-up score
vitamin B12	>👍👍👍👍
selenium	👍👍👍
vitamin A (total retinol equivalents)	👍👍
vitamin C	👍👍
phosphorus	👍👍
protein	👍👍
vitamin B6	👍
vitamin D	👍
niacin	👍
riboflavin	👍
folate	👍
calcium	👍
chloride	👍
copper	👍
iodine	👍
iron	👍
zinc	👍

Fish pie

Serves 4 (medium difficulty to prepare)

Fish pie is a nutritional powerhouse and surprisingly easy to pre-prepare for treatment days or when things might get a bit hectic or tiring. It's also easy to digest.

600 ml milk, full fat
1 onion, chopped
2 bay leaves
10 black peppercorns
3-4 blades of mace
a few stalks of parsley, whole
500 g salmon
500 g smoked haddock
500 g cod or haddock
75 g butter
75 g plain flour
a splash of white wine (optional)
100 ml double cream
7 to 8 large floury potatoes
1 to 2 tbsp butter
75 ml cream
150 g Cheddar, grated
nutmeg
salt & pepper

Put milk, onion, bay leaves, peppercorns, mace, parsley and a bit of salt & pepper in a saucepan and warm. Add the fish fillets, cover and simmer for 2 to 3 minutes then remove from heat and let stand.

Peel, chop and boil the potatoes then mash adding butter and cream until smooth and fluffy. Add half the cheese, season lightly and add a pinch of nutmeg to finish.

Remove the skin from the fillets and tear them into large chunks and place in a casserole. Strain the milk and fish liquid through a sieve into a jug.

Next make a roux* by melting butter in a medium saucepan and stir in the flour. Cook for about a minute on low heat then gradually add the infused milk, wine and cream, stirring over a medium heat for about 5 minutes. The sauce should be both smooth and thick. Season to taste.

Preheat oven to 170°Cf. Generously coat the fish with the sauce. Spoon or pipe the potato over the fish mixture. Start around the outside and ensure that the edges are well sealed with mash then work toward the centre. Fluff the surface with a fork and sprinkle with the remaining cheese.

Place the dish on a baking tray and bake for about 45 minutes or until the top is golden-brown. Allow to rest for 10 minutes before serving.

Each portion provides 95g protein and 1350kcals.

*see *The basics & extras*, page 285

nutrient	thumbs-up score
vitamin B6	>👍👍👍👍
vitamin B12 (by a factor of 10!)	>👍👍👍👍
vitamin A total retinol equivalents)	>👍👍👍👍
vitamin B6	>👍👍👍👍
iodine	>👍👍👍👍
phosphorus	>👍👍👍👍
protein	>👍👍👍👍
selenium	>👍👍👍👍
sodium	>👍👍👍👍
chloride	>👍👍👍👍
calcium	👍👍👍👍
vitamin D	👍👍👍
niacin	👍👍👍
riboflavin	👍👍👍
thiamin	👍👍👍
potassium	👍👍👍
vitamin C	👍👍
folate	👍👍
magnesium	👍👍
zinc	👍👍
copper	👍
fibre (non-starch polysaccaride)	👍
iron	👍

Lemon sole fillet tacos & salsa

Serves 4 (easy to prepare)

I first came across this dish at a famous cookery school in Cornwall. It's an absolute zinger and makes you think of delicate sole in a completely different way.

450 g lemon sole fillets, skinned
8 flour tortillas
¼ cup mayonnaise*

For the marinade

1 tsp ground cumin
1 tsp hot paprika
2 garlic cloves, puréed
juice of 1 lemon
salt & pepper

For the salsa

4 tomatoes, de-seeded & diced
1 small red onion, finely chopped
a small bunch of coriander, chopped
1 jalapeno, de-seeded & finely chopped

Warmed tortillas to serve

Mix the marinade then coat both sides of the fillets and leave for 20 to 30 minutes.

Mix the salsa together and season to taste. Gently warm the tortillas in a pan on low heat, about 15 seconds each side and wrap them to keep warm.

Preheat oven to grill (broil) and place the fillets under the grill for 3 to 4 minutes on one side only. Remove from the heat and break into chunks. Serve with the mayonnaise and salsa in separate bowls with the tortillas and build at leisure!

Each portion provides 29g protein and 530kcals.

*see *The basics & extras*, page 285

nutrient	thumbs-up score
vitamin B12	👍👍👍👍
selenium	👍👍👍👍
phosphorus	👍👍👍
sodium	👍👍👍
chloride	👍👍👍
protein	👍👍
vitamin C	👍
niacin	👍
thiamin	👍
calcium	👍
iron	👍

Grilled sardines with wasabi butter

Serves 4 (medium difficulty to prepare)

I love these little bundles of joy. Tiny fish, big flavour.

16 sardines, filleted
sea salt
200 g butter
1 tbsp wasabi powder or paste
1 garlic clove, puréed
freshly cracked black pepper

Make the butter by mixing the wasabi, garlic and a few turns of pepper into slightly softened butter. This can be rolled and sealed in cling film and returned to the fridge for storage until ready to use.

To fillet the sardines, snip the head by fins with scissors and cut the length of its underside and remove the innards. Gently pry open the sardine's cavity to butterfly the fish. Run your fingers along the fish's backbone to loosen it from the meat. Starting from the top to the tail, gently lift out the backbone and ribs and remove any stray bones. The tail should pull off with the bones.

Preheat bbq to hot or set oven to grill (broil).

Sprinkle salt inside and over the skin of the fish. Place on the bbq or under grill for 1 minute then gently turn and cook the other side. The skin should go lightly crispy. Serve hot garnished with pats of the wasabi butter.

A super accompaniment for these is the mediterranean fennel salad, see page 146.

Each portion provides 50g protein and 780kcals.

nutrient	thumbs-up score
vitamin B6	>👍👍👍👍
vitamin B12	>👍👍👍👍
vitamin D	>👍👍👍👍
phosphorus	>👍👍👍👍
selenium	>👍👍👍👍
protein	👍👍👍👍
vitamin A total retinol equivalents)	👍👍👍
niacin	👍👍👍
iodine	👍👍👍
sodium	👍👍👍
chloride	👍👍👍
riboflavin	👍
calcium	👍
copper	👍
iron	👍
magnesium	👍
potassium	👍
zinc	👍

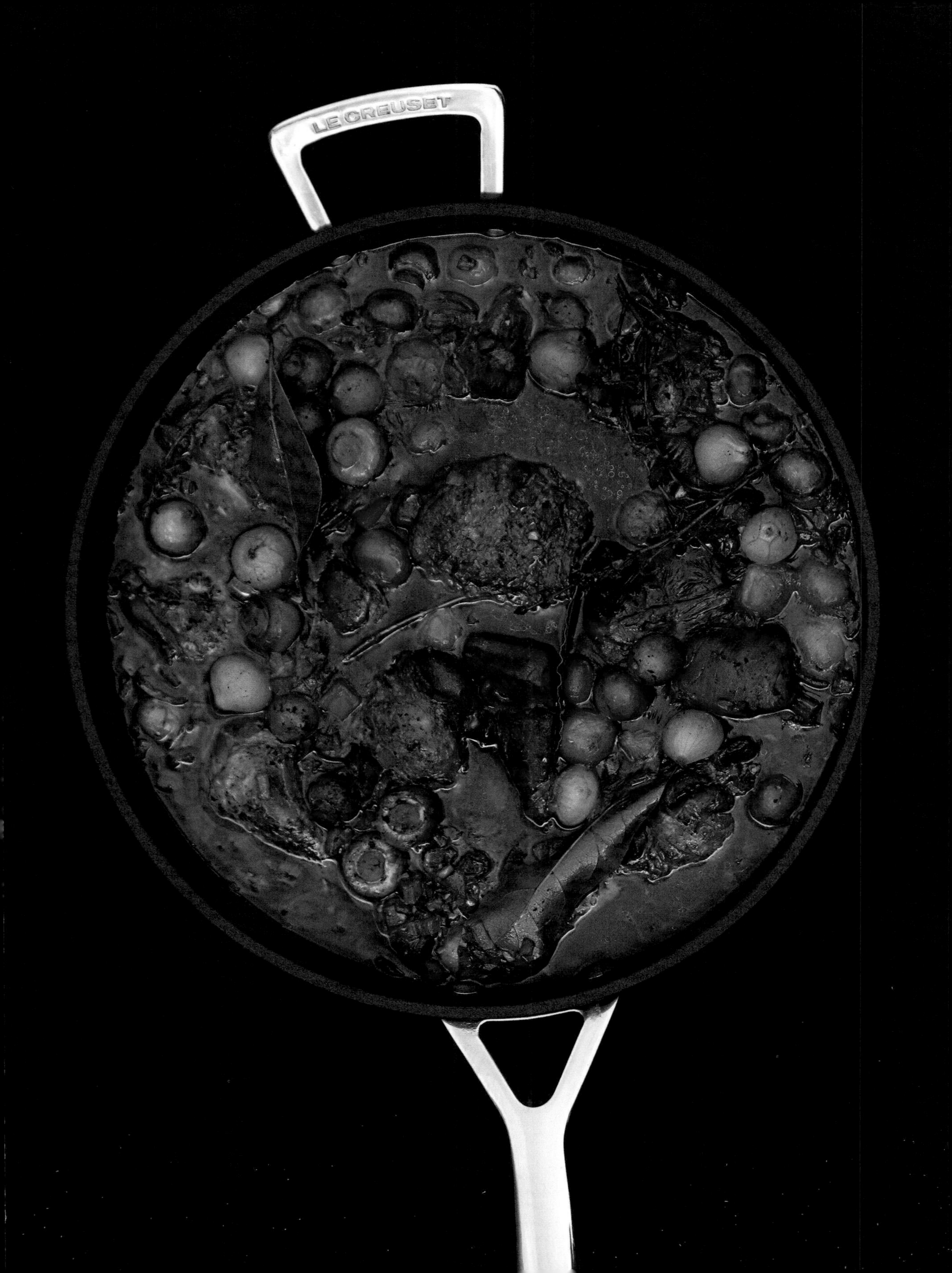
LE CREUSET

Coq au vin

Serves 4 (easy to prepare)

This is a great French classic. Preparing it all in one large pan keeps all the goodness in and really saves on the washing up.

1 large corn fed chicken, cut into pieces
150 g pancetta
30 g butter
2 medium onions, chopped
1 litre hot chicken stock
1 large carrot, chopped
2 stalks celery, chopped
2 to 3 garlic cloves, chopped
2 tbsp flour
50 ml brandy
1 bottle of wine, (Burgundy red or white)
4 to 5 sprigs thyme
3 bay leaves
40 g butter
12 pearl onions
200 g small button mushrooms

Cut the pancetta into small pieces and fry with butter in a deep pan. When golden lift the pancetta into a bowl leaving the fat.

Next season the chicken by rubbing it with salt & pepper and place them in the hot fat and sear them on all sides until golden. The colour of the skin is the key.

Place the chicken with the pancetta. Add the onion, celery, carrot and garlic to the pan. Stir and scrape the residue so that it coats the vegetables. If the mixture gets dry add a bit of stock.

Next return the chicken and pancetta to the pan and stir in flour. Cook for a few minutes then add the brandy and herbs. Finally cover the chicken with wine and stock then add mushrooms and pearl onions. Cover and let simmer for at least one hour or until the chicken is well cooked.

Remove the chicken from the pan to rest. Turn up the jus and reduce by half. Add a knob of butter and season to taste.

Each portion provides 120g protein and 940kcals.

nutrient	thumbs-up score
vitamin B6	>👍👍👍👍
vitamin B12	>👍👍👍👍
niacin	>👍👍👍👍
phosphorus	>👍👍👍👍
protein	>👍👍👍👍
sodium	>👍👍👍👍
selenium	👍👍👍👍
riboflavin	👍👍👍
copper	👍👍👍
zinc	👍👍👍
vitamin A (total retinol equivalents)	👍👍
magnesium	👍👍
potassium	👍👍
vitamin D	👍
thiamin	👍
chloride	👍
folate	👍
iodine	👍
iron	👍

Chicken, leek & mushroom chasseur

Serves 4, (medium difficulty to prepare)

This is such a comforting dish any time of year. Slow cook it well in advance so the meat is really tenderised. At home we call this 'chicken on a cloud'.

4 boneless chicken breasts, skinless & cubed
2 garlic cloves, smashed
2 shallots, finely diced
a splash of olive oil
a splash of brandy (optional)
salt & pepper

For the sauce

200 g button mushrooms
1 small leek, white only, thinly sliced
2 shallots, finely diced
175 ml chicken stock
120 ml white wine (or extra stock)
75 g crème fraîche
100 to 150 ml single cream, as required
1 tsp Dijon mustard
salt & pepper
a small bunch of curly parsley, finely chopped for garnish
a sprig of thyme for garnish
potato purée to serve (see page 180)

Heat the oil in a large frying pan on medium-high heat and add the garlic and shallots and cook without colour. Add the chicken cubes and cook through until nicely browned. When nearly done, if you fancy some drama, flambé with brandy or just add it to the meat and simmer for a minute. Remove from heat and set aside to rest.

Next deglaze the pan using a splash of the white wine. Add the mushrooms, shallots and leek and cook over medium heat until most of the moisture has evaporated. Now add the remainder of the wine and allow to simmer for a minute then add the chicken stock and allow to reduce by at least half on low heat. Stir in the sour cream and mustard and then slowly stir in the cream, allowing the sauce to reduce by half. Season to taste.

Add the chicken to the sauce to warm. When ready, serve over a potato purée and top with a sprig of thyme.

Each portion provides 26g protein and 410kcals.

nutrient	thumbs-up score
vitamin B12	>👍👍👍👍
vitamin B6	👍👍👍
sodium	👍👍👍
chloride	👍👍
niacin	👍👍
phosphorus	👍👍
protein	👍👍
vitamin A (total retinol equivalents)	👍
riboflavin	👍
copper	👍
potassium	👍
selenium	👍
zinc	👍

Turkey bubble & squeak

Serves as many as you have leftovers for (easy to prepare)

This little and often recipe can be made at any time of year by roasting a turkey leg and making a stove top stuffing.

equal parts of mashed potatoes, stuffing & chopped cooked turkey
1 egg yolk
1 onion, chopped
2 tbsp butter
a few Brussels sprouts or cabbage, cooked & chopped
2 tbsp olive oil
flour for breading the patties
leftover gravy (or use Bisto)

Place the potatoes, stuffing, turkey and egg yolk in a bowl and mix together. Melt the butter in a pan and sauté the onion without colour then add the sprouts or cabbage to warm through. Stir the vegetables into the turkey mixture. Form into patties and lightly flour.

Melt a generous knob of butter in a lightly oiled pan and fry the patties on medium heat until crispy golden, turn and crisp the other side. Warm the gravy and drizzle over the patties. Serve hot.

Each portion provides 22g protein and 440kcals.

nutrient	thumbs-up score
vitamin B12	👍👍👍
vitamin B6	👍👍
phosphorus	👍👍
protein	👍👍
vitamin A (total retinol equivalents)	👍
vitamin C	👍
folate	👍
niacin	👍
thiamin	👍
sodium	👍
chloride	👍
zinc	👍

Crispy duck pancakes

Serves 4 (easy to prepare)

The duck is so easy to prepare. A little goes a long way.

2 duck legs
2 to 3 handfuls of sea salt
freshly cracked black pepper
4 spring onions, julienned
½ cucumber, de-seeded & julienned

Hoisin sauce & Chinese pancake wraps

Preheat oven to 220°Cf. Rub the duck legs generously with salt and place in a deep metal roasting pan. Crack on pepper and place in hot oven for approximately 1 hour. When ready the skin will be dark golden and crackling crisp.

Remove from oven and shred the meat away from the bone with a fork. Serve immediately with onions, cucumber, pancakes and sauce.

Hoisin sauce

4 tbsp soy sauce
2 tbsp smooth peanut butter
1 tbsp dark brown sugar
2 tsp rice wine vinegar
1 garlic clove, finely minced
2 tsp sesame seed oil
1 tsp sriracha (or other hot sauce to taste)
a few cracks of fresh black pepper

Mix together all ingredients and keep refrigerated in an airtight container.

A single duck pancake, assembled on average provides 43g protein and 600kcals*.

nutrient	thumbs-up score
vitamin B6	>👍👍👍👍
vitamin B12	👍👍👍
phosphorus	👍
protein	👍
sodium	👍
chloride	👍
vitamin A (total retinol equivalents)	3%*
iodine	3%
vitamin C	5%
magnesium	5%
calcium	6%
potassium	6%
thiamin	8%
niacin	9%
copper	10%
iron	11%
selenium	14%
zinc	13%
riboflavin	18%

*In this recipe we have listed nutrients that don't quite make a full 'thumbs-up' in order to demonstrate how much additional nutritional value this snack or light meal contains.

Beef bourguignon ⚖

Serves 6 to 8 (easy to prepare)

This is possibly one of the best meals ever invented. As a slow cooked dish it really takes very little effort to produce a magnificent meal.

olive oil
3 garlic cloves, crushed
a dash of sriracha*
1 bottle red or white Burgundy wine
350 g steak, cubed
15 to 20 pearl onions, peeled
15 to 20 small button mushrooms
herbs de Provençe
2 tbsp Dijon mustard
salt & pepper
egg tagliatelle*
Parmesan cheese, finely grated
sliced baguette to serve & mop up the gravy

In a deep saucepan, warm the garlic and sriracha in a little olive oil. Splash in a little wine, add the beef then turn up the heat and sear all over. Reduce heat then add the onions, mushrooms and the rest of the wine. Simmer for at least an hour, adding salt, pepper and herbs to taste.

Then add the mustard, a few extra herbs and the rest of the wine and simmer for another hour. Stir from time to time and season to taste. Prepare the noodles al dente and rinse well. This is a communal dish so serve the pasta and beef in separate bowls with bread and cheese on the side and let everyone dive in.

Each portion provides 21g protein and 245kcals.

*see *The basics & extras*, page 285

nutrient	thumbs-up score
vitamin B12	👍👍👍
vitamin B6	👍👍
copper	👍👍
phosphorus	👍👍
iodine	👍
iron	👍
protein	👍
selenium	👍
sodium	👍
chloride	👍
zinc	👍

Cabbage rolls (golabki)

Serves 4 (medium difficulty to prepare)

This traditional Eastern European dish has as many variations as there are countries. Don't be put off by school meal memories of boiled cabbage. It's absolutely packed with flavour.

1 head of white cabbage
225 g long grain white rice, uncooked
3 garlic cloves, crushed
a dash of sriracha*
1 large onion, finely chopped
450 g beef mince
225 g pork mince
2 tbsp mixed herbs
1 tbsp paprika
3 tbsp Worcestershire sauce
2 eggs, beaten
salt & pepper
1 litre passata
400 g chopped tomatoes
salt & pepper

Remove the core from the cabbage and place in simmering water. As the cabbage softens remove the leaves being careful not to break them. This will take about 40 minutes. The innermost leaves will be too small to use and can be finely chopped and added to the meat mixture. The cabbage is hot, so take precautions.

To make the filling, cook the rice and warm the garlic and chilli paste in an oiled skillet. Add onions and cook without colour. Sauté the mince with the garlic and onions and add herbs, paprika and Worcestershire sauce. Season to taste. When fully cooked, add the meat and rice together then stir in the eggs. Check the seasoning.

For the sauce add passata, tomatoes, garlic and seasoning together in a pan. Allow to simmer for about 20 minutes.

Preheat oven to 160°Cf. To make the rolls, place a scoop of the meat into the centre of a cabbage leaf and roll, then place opening down into a casserole. Ladle the sauce over the rolls and bake in a low oven for an hour.

Each portion provides 46g protein and 840kcals.

* see *The basics & extras,* page 285

nutrient	thumbs-up score
vitamin A (total retinol equivalents)	>👍👍👍👍
vitamin B6	>👍👍👍👍
vitamin B12	>👍👍👍👍
phosphorous	👍👍👍👍
protein	👍👍👍👍
sodium	👍👍👍👍
chloride	👍👍👍👍
vitamin C	👍👍👍
niacin	👍👍👍
thiamin	👍👍👍
iron	👍👍👍
zinc	👍👍👍
potassium	👍👍
vitamin D	👍
riboflavin	👍
calcium	👍
copper	👍
fibre (as non-starch polysaccharide)	👍
folate	👍
iodine	👍
magnesium	👍
selenium	👍

Escalope of pork with juniper & Marsala ⚖

Serves 4 (medium difficulty to prepare)

Flavours and ingredients straight out of the Sicilian hills. Use the leanest and finest pork loins you can find. It's simply bursting with flavour. I would serve this with green vegetables or taglietelle.

25 g dried porcini mushrooms
10 dried juniper berries
4 lean pork escalopes
10 ml balsamic vinegar
a knob of butter
8 garlic cloves
45 ml Marsala
3 to 4 sprigs of fresh rosemary
salt & pepper

Place the porcini in a bowl and just cover with hot water. Do the same for the juniper berries in a separate bowl. Leave for 30 minutes. Strain both, reserving the mushroom liquid only. Crush the berries with the side of a knife and set aside until ready to use.

If the escalopes are quite thick you may want to pound them out with a meat mallet. Place each escalope between a layer of cling film. Pound to 1 cm thickness (this stage is optional). Brush the escalopes with vinegar.

Melt the butter with a drop of oil in a large pan on medium high heat. Brown the escalopes on one side then flip and fry for a further minute, no more. Add the garlic, Marsala, rosemary, mushrooms & berries with the remaining vinegar. Season and allow to gently simmer on low heat for 3 minutes. Add a splash of the mushroom liquid if the Marsala jus becomes a bit dry. Season to taste and serve immediately.

Each portion provides 15g protein and 150kcals.

nutrient	thumbs-up score
thiamin	👍👍
vitamin B6	👍
vitamin B12	👍
niacin	👍
sodium	👍
chloride	👍
protein	👍
phosphorus	👍

Simon's pie

Serves 4 to 6 (easy to medium difficulty to prepare)

I made this dish up from leftover Sunday dinner when Simon was on chemotherapy. It's a super nutritious take on shepherd's pie.

To prepare the lamb

4 lamb shanks
2 tsp olive oil
1 bottle of red wine
6 garlic cloves
2 onions, chopped
a generous handful of mixed herbs
500 ml lamb stock
a dash of sriracha*
salt & pepper
3 bay leaves

For the pie

1.25 kg potatoes
2 to 3 tsp white plain flour
100 ml water, approximately
200 g shallots, finely chopped
800 g pre-cooked puy lentils, 2 tins
nutmeg

Slow cook the lamb and ingredients on medium for 6 to 8 hours.

The meat should fall off the bone. When ready, strain the jus through a fine sieve. Pull the meat from the bones ensuring there is no fat.

Next boil and mash potatoes and season with salt, pepper and nutmeg. To make the gravy, bring the jus to hard boil then reduce heat to simmer. Using flour and water, make a smooth paste and whisk into the jus avoiding lumps. Bring back to the boil. Season to taste.

Preheat oven to 170°Cf. Layer the lentils, shallots and lamb in a casserole. Add sufficient gravy to completely cover the meat then cover with a generous layer of potatoes adding seasoning and a dash of nutmeg. Seal to the edges to prevent the sauce from boiling over. Rough up the surface using a fork. Bake until golden brown on top. Remove from heat and leave to rest for 10 minutes before serving.

Each portion provides 77g protein and 1080kcals.

* see *The basics & extras,* page 285

nutrient	thumbs-up score
vitamin B6	>👍👍👍👍
vitamin B12	>👍👍👍👍
copper	>👍👍👍👍
iron	>👍👍👍👍
phosporous	>👍👍👍👍
protein	>👍👍👍👍
selenium	>👍👍👍👍
zinc	>👍👍👍👍
thiamin	👍👍👍👍
fibre (non-starch polysaccharide)	👍👍👍👍
vitamin C	👍👍👍
folate	👍👍👍
niacin	👍👍👍
magnesium	👍👍👍
riboflavin	👍👍
sodium	👍👍
chloride	👍👍
calcium	👍

Welsh cawl

Serves 4 (medium difficulty to prepare)

This national treasure of Wales is a showcase of winter veg and surprisingly light as the broth is not thickened. My Welsh neighbour insists it should be served with a wedge of Caerphilly cheese and a chunk of wholegrain bread.

500 g lamb shoulder
60 ml sunflower oil
1 onion
2 carrots
½ swede
1 parsnip
½ small celeriac or 2 celery sticks
¼ small white cabbage, finely shredded
sprigs of parsley & thyme
2 ½ litres lamb stock
1 leek, white only
1 large potato, peeled
salt & pepper

Cut the meat into 1 inch pieces, removing fat and sinew.

Peel and dice the root vegetables into uniform and small pieces. Clean the leek and finely chop this along with the onion and celeriac.

Next, on medium heat, coat a large saucepan with oil then add the meat and brown. Remove the meat then add the onion and cook without colour. (Browning the onion will make it bitter.)

Return the meat to the pan and add the carrot, swede, parsnip, and celeriac. Mix well and cover with stock.

Bring to the boil and add the parsley and thyme. Simmer for about an hour, adding the potato and leek after 30 minutes and more stock or water if required. Simmer until the potatoes and leeks are soft.

Season to taste and serve with cheese and bread.

Each portion provides 22g protein and 330kcals.

nutrient	thumbs-up score
sodium	>👍👍👍👍
chloride	>👍👍👍👍
vitamin B12	👍👍👍👍
vitamin B6	👍👍👍
vitamin C	👍👍
phosphorus	👍👍
protein	👍👍
zinc	👍👍
folate	👍
niacin	👍
thiamin	👍
copper	👍
potassium	👍

Ginger & pepper cake with salted toffee sauce & clotted cream
see page 257

Puddings

Stacked mangos & raspberry coulis

Lemon possett

Chocolate & beetroot tart

Chocolate silk pie

Limoncello gelato

Auntie Winona's brownies

Ginger & pepper cake with salted toffee sauce

Victoria sandwich

Champagne soused raspberry jelly

Baked apple with cinnamon ice cream

Plum frangipane tart

Pink & pineapple fluff

Two little pots – demi et demi

Something sweet

sugar, dairy & empty calories

Something sweet to finish a meal can be a real reward and comfort. Just as an aperitif to start a meal can stimulate the appetite, a digestif can calm and aid digestion. When we are in full health we often worry about adding unnecessary calories to already rich diets but when appetite is diminished we need to adjust our perception.

You may have heard the term 'empty calories' used to describe any high sugar or high fat foods that don't contain substantial essential nutrients. You might also be familiar with the saying, 'I've never met a calorie I didn't like!' These foods are frequently processed fast foods and between meal snacks. If you're watching your weight, being cautious about empty calorie foods is a good idea but if your appetite is poor, they could be a godsend!

In recipes, ingredients that add sugar or fat can be important for flavour and ultimately how much you enjoy the food; an important part of the recipe's flavour profile. If your appetite is poor and you need to pack more calories into a small portion, adding sugar, butter, oil or cream maybe just what you need until you are able to eat larger portions to meet your nutritional needs. So, far from being just 'empty calories', these foods could be the stars of the show!

I hope I don't confuse too many fellow bakers in this section. I haven't been consistent in the use of metric and empirical measures. Some recipes are in grams and milliliters and where I've used cups and teaspoons it's because the recipe comes from a different country or era and works perfectly as it is. I hope you don't mind.

Get moving

It's a stretch

If you only have the energy for one thing, stretch! When you're weary and sore, it's easy to find a position that's least uncomfortable and stay there for quite a while. That, combined with a self-protective tendency to huddle up, can leave you tight and aching in places that have never bothered you in the past.

Stretching before bed, along with some easy breathing exercises, will soothe your spirits and lengthen tight muscles.

You'll sleep more comfortably and wake up feeling better.

Go to page 323 for some stretches to try.

Looking good feels better

Hair with flair!

Hair loss and changes in hair growth aren't restricted to your head, so you may want to learn how to re-create your eyes – subtly or with a bit of flair! I don't recommend the use of heavy make-up and once your eyelashes have gone falsies can be difficult to maintain but, hey, go for it if they work for you and waterproof brow and eyeliner can look great.

Seek out a local beauty centre that specialises in advice during and after cancer treatment; you'll be amazed at how uplifting a bit of expert TLC can be.

Stacked mangos & raspberry coulis

Serves 4 (medium difficulty to prepare)

This dessert is so fresh. If ripe mangos are hard to find, tinned will work.

1 to 2 sheets filo pastry
40 g butter, melted
2 ripe mangoes
raspberry coulis*
icing sugar

Preheat oven to 170°Cf. Lay a filo pastry sheet on a clean work surface. Use a scone cutter to make twelve 10 cm rounds. Place on a non-stick baking sheet and brush lightly with butter. Bake in the oven until crisp and very lightly golden. Carefully transfer to a wire rack to cool.

Peel the mangoes and carefully cut into slices around the stones. If using tinned, drain and pat dry.

To assemble the dish, lay a filo pastry disk on 4 plates then a layer of mango and a drizzle of coulis. Repeat this twice more then top with remaining mango and coulis. Dust with icing sugar and serve.

Each portion provides 2g protein and 160kcals.

* see *The basics* & extras, page 285

nutrient	thumbs-up score
vitamin C	👍👍👍👍
vitamin A (total retinol equivalents)	👍👍

Lemon posset

Serves 4 (easy to prepare)

Though it's not a nutritional giant this is so fresh and palette cleansing and the creamy lemon cuts through plastic mouth and is easy to swallow. It's frequently served with lemon shortbread. Mmmmm.

600 ml double cream
150 g granulated sugar
juice & zest of 2 lemons
fresh raspberries for garnish

Over low heat bring the cream and sugar just to the boil and simmer for 3 minutes. The sugar should be completely dissolved. Whisk in the lemon juice and zest and pour into glasses and chill until ready to serve.

Be careful when zesting the lemon to take only the yellow of the skin, the white is bitter.

Each portion provides 3g protein and 890kcals.

nutrient	thumbs-up score
vitamin A (total retinol equivalents)	>👍👍👍👍
riboflavin	👍
iodine	👍

Chocolate & beetroot tart

Yields 1, 9 inch tart (easy to prepare)

This is a clever way to get one of your best friends, beetroot, into the mix (literally). The natural sugar of the beetroot has an earthier flavour and also gives this tart a very moist texture. If you don't tell anyone they won't notice!

100 g dark chocolate
100 g butter, melted
300 g light brown sugar
3 eggs
225 g flour
50 g dry cocoa
¼ tsp salt
250 g beetroot, cooked, peeled & grated

Preheat oven to 170°Cf. Line a 22 cm square loose-bottomed cake tin with parchment.

Melt 75 g of the chocolate over simmering water and finely chop the rest.

Mix together the butter, sugar and eggs until the sugar is completely dissolved. Stir in the melted chocolate. Sift together the flour, cocoa and salt, then fold into the chocolate mixture.

Finally, stir in the beetroot and chopped chocolate. Pour into the cake tin and bake for about 20 to 25 minutes until a toothpick comes out almost clean.

Allow to cool for 5 minutes, then remove from the tin.
Serve with a tablespoon of crème fraîche for a bit more luxury.

Each portion provides 16g protein and 1070kcals.

nutrient	thumbs-up score
vitamin A (total retinol equivalents)	👍👍👍
vitamin B12	👍👍👍
copper	👍👍👍
phosphorus	👍👍👍
vitamin B6	👍👍
iron	👍👍
magnesium	👍👍
sodium	👍👍
chloride	👍
folate	👍
riboflavin	👍
calcium	👍
fibre (non-starch polysaccaride)	👍
iodine	👍
potassium	👍
protein	👍
zinc	👍

Chocolate silk pie

Yields 1, 9 inch pie (medium difficult to prepare)

Chocolate silk pie, even the name has a bit of 'come hither' about it. If you fancy smooth and elegant chocolate this is just the ticket.

For the crust

275 g graham or digestive biscuit crumbs
50 g butter

For the topping

150 g whipping cream
chocolate shavings

For the filling

150 g butter, softened
2 tsp pure vanilla
200 g caster sugar
90 g baking chocolate, unsweetened
3 large eggs

Prepare the crust by melting the butter and stirring in the biscuit crumbs. Press into a 9 inch spring form pan or individual moulds and chill.

To make the filling, cream the butter and vanilla in a large mixing bowl with a hand mixer at medium to high speed for about 1 minute. Gradually add the sugar while continuing to beat until the mixture is light and fluffy and not granular – this will take several minutes and is essential to the success of the recipe.

Melt the chocolate in bowl over a pan of boiling water. Add to the butter mixture beating until the chocolate is well blended and the mixture is smooth and creamy.

Finally, add the eggs one at a time, beating in each before adding the next until the mixture is light and fluffy. Pour the filling into the crust, smooth the top and then chill for several hours until set. When set top with whipped cream and chocolate shavings.

Each portion provides 39g protein and 471kcals.

nutrient	thumbs-up score
vitamin B6	👍👍👍
vitamin A (total retinol equivalents)	👍👍
vitamin B12	👍👍
sodium	👍
chloride	👍

Limoncello gelato

Serves 4 (easy to prepare)

I get asked for this more than any other dessert. It's a little taste bud tingling jewel. The limoncello gives it mouth-watering flavour. It is soothing on the throat as well.

juice & zest of 3 large lemons
190 g icing sugar
450 ml double cream
3 tbsp limoncello, frozen

Place the lemon zest and juice in a bowl. Add the icing sugar, stir to combine and leave for 30 minutes. Whip the cream and limoncello to soft peaks, then add the lemon and sugar mixture and whip together. Freeze overnight. Spoon the mixture into glasses or hollowed-out lemon halves to serve.

Each portion provides 2g protein and 790kcals.

nutrient	thumbs-up score
vitamin A (total retinol requirements)	>👍👍👍👍
vitamin B6	>👍👍👍👍
vitamin B12	👍👍
iodine	👍

Auntie Winona's brownies

Serves 4 (easy to prepare)

These brownies are moist and sooo chocolatey! A real pick me up.

½ cup cocoa (add a splash of hot water)
1 cup icing sugar
½ cup butter, softened
2 eggs
½ cup flour
1 tsp vanilla extract
a pinch of salt

For the icing

2 tbsp butter
2 tbsp cocoa
2 cups icing sugar
1 tsp vanilla extract
a pinch of salt
½ cup walnuts, chopped

Heat the oven to 170°Cf. Cream the butter, sugar and cocoa. Add the remaining ingredients and mix until smooth and creamy. Pour into a 22 cm square, (9 x 9) greased and floured cake tin and bake for 20 to 30 minutes or a toothpick comes out clean.

For the icing put all ingredients in a bowl and whip together until smooth. Ice the brownies and sprinkle with chopped walnuts.

Each portion provides 10g protein and 1230kcals.

nutrient	thumbs-up score
vitamin A (total retinol equivalents)	👍👍👍👍
copper	👍👍👍
sodium	👍👍👍
chloride	👍👍
vitamin B6	👍👍
phosphorus	👍👍
iodine	👍
iron	👍
magnesium	👍
zinc	👍

Ginger & pepper cake with salted toffee sauce — see illustration on page 244

Serves 8 (easy to prepare)

This cake is beautiful and indulgent. The combination of pepper, ginger, salt and caramel can really wake up tastebuds.

100 g butter, plus extra to grease
100 g light muscovado sugar
175 g self-raising flour
4 tsp ground ginger
1tsp white pepper
85 g golden syrup
85 g maple syrup
3 tbsp ginger wine liqueur or brandy
2 free-range eggs, beaten
1 inch fresh ginger, peeled & finely grated
150 g candied ginger, finely chopped
a pinch of salt
clotted cream or vanilla ice cream to serve

Preheat the oven to 160°Cf and grease and line a 22 cm loaf or bundt tin. Cream together the butter and sugar with a pinch of salt until fluffy. Sift together the flour and ground ginger.

Pour in the golden syrup (the easiest way to handle the syrup is with a lightly greased spoon and a silicone spatula) and 1 tbsp wine and mix to combine.

Beat in the eggs, a little at a time then gradually mix in the flour. Finally, stir through the fresh and candied ginger and spoon into the prepared tin. Level the top and bake for about 50 to 60 minutes until a toothpick into the centre comes out clean.

Allow to cool in the tin. When it's completely cool, make the icing by mixing together the icing sugar and remaining ginger wine and drizzle over the top of the cake. Slice the stem ginger thinly and arrange down the centre of the cake.

Salted toffee sauce

300 ml double cream
85 g butter, diced
100 g light muscovado sugar
1 tsp sea salt flakes

Put the cream, butter and sugar in a saucepan. Melt together, then bubble, stirring, until toffee-coloured and saucy. Add salt to taste. Serve warm.

Each portion (including a portion of the salted toffee sauce) provides 4g protein and 675kcals.

nutrient	thumbs-up score
vitamin A (total retinol equivalents)	👍👍👍👍
vitamin B12	👍👍
sodium	👍
chloride	👍
calcium	👍
phosphorus	👍
iodine	👍
iron	👍
magnesium	👍
zinc	👍

Victoria sandwich

Yield: 1 20 cm cake – 8 portions (medium difficulty to prepare)

This English classic was in its heyday during the war as most of the ingredients could be easily acquired such as foraged raspberries or blackberries for the conserve, eggs and even cream to make the butter. It's as luscious today as ever it was.

200 g caster sugar
200 g butter, softened
4 eggs, beaten
200 g self-raising flour
1 tsp baking powder
2 tbsp milk
raspberry conserve
icing sugar

Buttercream icing

140 g butter, softened
280 g icing sugar
½ tsp vanilla extract (optional)

Preheat oven to 170ºCf and butter and flour the sandwich tins (or butter and line with baking parchment). In a large bowl, cream together the butter and sugar then add the eggs and continue to beat until creamy. Add in the flour and beat until the batter is light and fluffy. Divide the batter between the two tins and smooth the surface with a spoon. Bake for about 20 minutes until the cake springs back to the touch. Turn onto a cooking rack and leave to cool completely.

For the buttercream icing, beat the butter in a large bowl until soft. Add half of the icing sugar and beat until smooth. Add the vanilla and remaining icing sugar and beat the mixture until creamy and smooth. If the icing gets too stiff beat in a few drops of milk.

To build the sandwich, smooth a generous layer of buttercream onto one of the cakes followed by an equally generous layer of conserve. Cover the second cake with a dusting of icing sugar and place on top.

Each portion provides 6g protein and 750kcals.

nutrient	thumbs-up score
vitamin A (total retinol equivalents)	👍👍👍
vitamin B12	👍👍
phosphorus	👍👍
chloride	👍
sodium	👍
iodine	👍

Champagne soused raspberry jelly

Serves 4 (easy to prepare)

This is a playful pudding and the raspberries tingle the taste buds. If you don't want residual alcohol, soak the berries in water then simply plop them in at the end.

600 ml Champagne (cava or proscecco are fine)*
120 g sugar
8 sheets (20 g) leaf gelatin
a punnet of fresh raspberries
300 ml whipping cream (optional)

Place 4 jelly glasses or moulds into fridge to chill. Next pour the wine into a bowl with the raspberries, saving a few for garnish, and allow to soak for 1 to 2 hours.

Place the gelatin leaves in cold water to allow to soften.

Pour the Champagne into a saucepan through a fine sieve keeping the berries. Place the liquid on medium heat and add the sugar stirring constantly until sugar is fully dissolved. Do not allow the mixture to boil. Remove the gelatin from the water and add to the Champagne mixture and stir until completely dissolved. Remove from heat.

Place the berries into the chilled glasses (moulds) and fill with the liquid. Place in the fridge for several hours until firmly set. Serve cold with whipped cream and a few fresh berries.

Each portion (including the cream) provides 6g protein and 540kcals.

**If you want to substitute the Champagne, you can use white grape juice but remember that when cooking the wine, the alcohol evaporates.*

nutrient	thumbs-up score
vitamin C	👍👍
vitamin A (total retinol equivalents)	👍

Baked apples & cinnamon ice cream

Serves 4, 1 apple per person (very easy to prepare)

Comfort food! This is great on a cool winter evening.

For the apples

4 apples, tart & firm such as braeburn or mackintosh
butter
cinnamon sticks

For the cinnamon ice cream

225 ml milk
1 cinnamon stick
3 egg yolks
100 g sugar
1 tsp ground cinnamon
450 ml whipping or double cream

Prepare the ice cream well in advance. At least 3 hours. Put the milk in a pan with the cinnamon stick and bring to the boil. In a separate bowl, whisk together the egg yolks, sugar and ground cinnamon. Discard the cinnamon stick, then strain the hot milk over the yolks, whisking continuously. (For a quick cheat add ground cinnamon and a bit of brown sugar to vanilla ice cream).

Pour the mixture into a well-chilled bowl. Freeze for 1½ hours or until starting to freeze. Stir well, then repeat the process twice more until the mixture is smooth. Transfer to a sealed container and keep frozen until ready to serve.

Preheat oven to 170°Cf. Cut individual sheets of tin foil large enough to wrap each apple and smear with soft butter.

Core the apples and insert a cinnamon stick. Place on the buttered foil and dust with ground cinnamon. Wrap and seal to create a loose parcel. Bake for 15 to 20 minutes. Serve immediately with cinnamon ice cream.

Each portion provides 7g protein and 700kcals.

nutrient	thumbs-up score
vitamin B6	>👍👍👍👍
vitamin B12	>👍👍👍👍
vitamin A (total retinol equivalents)	👍👍👍👍
riboflavin	👍
calcium	👍
iodine	👍
phosphorus	👍

Plum frangipane tart

Yields 1, 23cm tart (medium difficulty to prepare)

nutrient	thumbs-up score
vitamin B12	>👍👍👍👍
vitamin A (total retinol equivalents)	👍👍👍👍
vitamin B6	👍👍👍
phosphorus	👍👍👍
riboflavin	👍👍
copper	👍👍
magnesium	👍👍
folate	👍
thiamin	👍
calcium	👍
fibre (as non-starch polysaccharide)	👍
iodine	👍
iron	👍
potassium	👍
protein	👍
sodium	👍
chloride	👍
zinc	👍

There's more to this luscious tart than it seems. Its packed with vitamins and nutrients and the plums pack a flavour wallop.

500 g ready-made puff pastry
100 g butter
225 g ground almonds
5 eggs
250 ml single cream
225 g golden caster sugar
6 to 15 plums depending on size, halved & stoned
2 tbsp Demerara sugar

Preheat oven to 170°Cf. Prepare the puff pastry in a loose-bottomed tart tin or individual tartlets. Chill for 30 minutes then blind bake, remove from the oven and allow to cool.

Melt the butter in a saucepan then whisk in the almonds, eggs, cream and sugar until smooth. Pour into the pastry case. Arrange the plums cut-side down, pushing them into the mixture. They should fit fairly close together or use ½ plum per tartlet. Sprinkle with the sugar and bake for 25 to 30 minutes or until the filling is just set and the plums are cooked. (The tartlets should take about half the time so keep an eye on them.)

Each portion provides 20g protein and 910kcals.

Pink & pineapple fluff

Serves 4 (medium difficulty to prepare)

Sometimes old-fashioned puddings are the best. This bit of frippery makes everyone smile. There are a few stages to this recipe so you'll need to prepare in advance.

1 litre cranberry juice
2 tbsp sugar
7 leaves of gelatin
300 ml whipping cream
2 tbsp sugar
300 ml pineapple, puréed
100 ml raspberry coulis*
small fresh strawberries, tops removed & sliced

Set out 4 clean parfait glasses and a container large enough to hold ½ litre. Place a clean glass bowl for whipping the cream in the fridge to chill.

Pour the cranberry juice into a saucepan, add the sugar and warm on medium-low heat. Meanwhile, soak the gelatin leaves in a bowl of cold water. When the juice is simmering place the softened gelatin into the juice one leaf at a time and stir until completely dissolved. Pour half the liquid into the container and portion out the rest evenly in the parfait glasses. Place in the refrigerator and leave for a couple hours until firmly set.

When the jelly is set, whip the cream with sugar and divide in half. Roughly whip in the set jelly then carefully spoon this in equal layers into the parfait glasses then add a layer of strawberries.

Fold the pineapple purée into the second half of the whipping cream and spoon this on top of the strawberries. Place back in the fridge for another half hour or until ready to serve. Garnish with a whole strawberry and serve chilled.

Each portion provides 10g protein and 580kcals.

* see *The basics & extras,* page 285

nutrient	thumbs-up score
vitamin C	>👍👍👍👍
vitamin A (total retinol equivalents)	👍👍👍

Two little pots – demi et demi ⚖

Serves 6 to 8 (easy to prepare)

Half & half, little & often – a bit of each. This is my simple take on an old-fashioned French classic. If you're feeling ambitious there's a recipe for delicate orange tuile biscuits to serve alongside and if you really want to push the boat out add a chocolate covered strawberry*!*

For the chocolate pot

½ cup sugar
⅓ cup cocoa
3 tbsp cornstarch
¼ tsp salt
2½ cups milk

In a saucepan mix together the dry ingredients then add the milk over medium-low heat. Stir constantly with a wooden spoon until bubbling and thick. Pour into ramekins cover with cling film and let cool. Store covered in the refrigerator.

For the vanilla pot

⅓ cup sugar
3 tbsp cornstarch
¼ tsp salt
2 cups milk
2 large egg yolks, slightly beaten
2 tbsp butter, softened
1 tsp vanilla extract
1 vanilla pod, split lengthwise & seeds removed

In a saucepan, mix together the sugar, cornstarch and salt. Gradually stir in the milk and pop in the de-seeded vanilla pod. Cook over medium-low heat, stirring constantly until mixture thickens and boils. Boil and continue to stir for 1 minute. Discard the vanilla pod.

Gradually stir half the hot mixture into the beaten egg yolks then stir this back into the remaining hot mixture in the saucepan. Bring back to the boil and stir for another minute then remove from the heat and stir in the butter and vanilla and vanilla seeds.

Pour into ramekins, cover with cling film and refrigerate about 1 hour or until chilled. Store covered in refrigerator.

Each portion provides 7g protein and 300kcals.

* see *The basics & extras,* page 285

nutrient	thumbs-up score
vitamin B12	>👍👍👍👍
phosphorus	👍👍
calcium	👍
riboflavin	👍
iodine	👍
magnesium	👍

Slush
See page 272

Cocktails & mocktails

Slush

Northern sunset

Frozen strawberry margarita

Gin & tonic ice lollies

Iced chai latte

Chocolate & mint yoghurt shake

Apple à la mode

Frozen watermelon with ginger & lime ice

Colour me pink
Tastebud tinglers

It can be tricky to understand whether alcohol is friend or foe when it comes to cancer. Alcohol is associated with cancer risk – the more you drink, the greater your risk but it's not as black and white as that when consumed in moderation.

Having a drink with friends can be uplifting and can also be part of your family and food tradition. Many cultures enjoy a pre-dinner drink. An aperitif is taken specifically to whet the appetite for what is to come.

The most important thing is to follow the professional medical advice you're given that is specific to you and use common sense.

If you're trying to control your weight, you can save calories by enjoying your cocktail as a mocktail!

If you're sensitive to roughage such as seeds and piths and using fresh fruit like strawberries, once liquidised, pass through a fine sieve and if you'd prefer to avoid the alcohol these drinks are still delicious without it. All of these mixtures can be frozen in ice cube trays or lolly moulds to make small snacks and they can be soothing on dry and tender mouths and also give your appetite a lift when it needs it.

Get moving

Strong arm

Sitting down with a drink? If breast cancer treatment has left you with lymphoedema in one or both arms, this is a good time to slot in some targeted exercises, which are recommended by Cancer Research UK.

You can do these while you're watching television, sitting at the kitchen table or even in bed.

If you have a compression sleeve, you should wear it. If any exercises make your arms ache, reduce the number of repetitions and aim to progress gradually. If any of them are too difficult, talk to your medical team or physio about it.

Turn to page 327 to find out how.

Looking good feels better

Hair we go again!

Not everyone in treatment loses their hair and the availability of specialised treatments such as cold caps have had a huge impact but if you're not one of the lucky ones, don't be hard on yourself. Specialist hairstylists are there to hold your hand through the whole journey.

When your hair grows back it is likely to do so in stages, the first regrowth is usually very fine and soft and can even be a different colour. Eventually and for most it will return to its original state. This can be a wonderful time to try a few new looks. Go on – give it a go!

Slush — See illustration on page 268

Serves 4 (easy to prepare)

You can keep portions of slush in the freezer and help yourself to a scoop whenever you fancy. It's wonderful to have on hand on warm afternoons.

3 bananas
2 apples
250 ml orange juice
250 ml pineapple juice
250 ml lemonade (juice)
lemonade (Sprite) or
    ginger beer for serving
ice cubes

Purée the bananas, apples and juices in a blender. Pour into a sealable container and freeze. When ready to serve pop a couple ice cubes in a large glass and half fill with lemonade or ginger beer (or fizzy wine for adults) then plop in a scoop or two of the frozen slush. Serve immediately.

Each portion provides 2g protein and 180kcals.

nutrient	thumbs-up score
vitamin C	>👍👍👍👍
vitamin B6	👍

Northern sunset

Serves 4 (easy to prepare)

This is an old family recipe. It's an interesting twist on mulled cider. It conjures memories of après ski and glowing fires.

500 ml apple cider
250 ml cranberry juice
3 to 4 tsp instant coffee
1 tbsp brown sugar
3 cloves
1 cinnamon stick
a splash of orange juice
a strip of orange peel
1 measure per serving of brandy
    or rum (optional)

Pour the cider and juice into a large saucepan and warm over medium-low heat. Stir in the coffee and brown sugar and drop in the cloves and cinnamon stick. Simmer for a few minutes then add the orange juice and peel. Serve hot.

Each portion provides 1g protein and 120kcals.

nutrient	thumbs-up score
vitamin C	👍👍👍

Frozen strawberry margaritas

Yields approximately 1.5 litres (easy to prepare)

This lovely concoction was invented in Tijuana in the 1940s. You can replace the strawberry with any fruit you want.

50 ml strawberry purée
40 ml gold tequila
20 ml Triple Sec or Cointreau
20 ml lemon or orange juice
ice

Coat the rim of a wide-mouthed glass by running a wedge of lemon around it then sprinkling with sugar. Place all the ingredients with a generous handful of ice in a blender and blitz until ice is fully crushed. Pour into glass and serve immediately.

For the strawberry purée, place 300 g trimmed strawberries and a pinch of sugar in a blender and liquidate. Pass through a sieve to remove pips.

To make a virgin margarita simply replace the tequila and triple sec with a bit more orange juice.

Each portion provides 0g protein and 180kcals.

nutrient	thumbs-up score
vitamin C	>👍👍👍👍

Gin & tonic ice lollies

Makes 6 large or 8 small (easy to prepare)

These aren't quite nutritional giants but they can stimulate appetite and soothe a sore mouth and throat. There's a bit of fun factor as well.

6 tbsp gin (or vodka)
375 ml sugar syrup*
375 ml tonic water
1 lime (or lemon)

Zest and juice the lime then strain the juice. Mix together the gin, sugar syrup, tonic water and juice. Pour into lolly moulds, allowing 1cm clearance at the top and freeze overnight.

If you want the flavour but not the alcohol you can infuse the sugar syrup by heating it with a few juniper berries.

Apparently this is a number one hit in the Marie Curie kitchens!

No protein but a real morale booster and posh way to help with dry mouth and nausea and to stimulate appetite. Bring it on.

One lolly provides 359kcals and 0g protein.

* see *The basics & extras, page 285*

It's not always about nutrition. Sometimes you just need a bit of fun.

nutrient thumbs-up score

Sorry, we couldn't analyse this recipe, it only gets a thumbs-up for fun!>

Iced chai latte ⚖

Serves 4 (easy to prepare)

This is a spicier and less sweet version of the coffee shop variety and it's great to have on hand. Its great just as tea hot or cold, the milk isn't essential to enjoy a nice cooler.

1 litre water
6 black tea bags
⅓ cup honey
5 green cardamom pods
¼ tsp ground cinnamon
10 whole cloves
1 inch ginger, peeled & coarsely chopped
a pinch of pepper
2 cups cold milk (almond or goats' milk are good substitutes)

Bring the water to the boil. Remove from heat and stir in the tea bags. Cover and let steep for 5 minutes. Remove the tea bags. Stir in the honey and spices until honey is dissolved. Allow to cool a bit and then cover and refrigerate until cold. Stir before serving to mix in the spices that have settled on the bottom.

For a pitcher full: stir 2 cups milk directly into the cold tea. Pour into glasses over ice.

For individual servings: Fill the glass with ice. Top with $^{2}/_{3}$ cup cold tea and then with $^{1}/_{3}$ cup milk. Stir to serve.

Each portion provides 5g protein and 140 kcals.

nutrient	thumbs-up score
vitamin B12	👍👍👍
riboflavin	👍
calcium	👍
iodine	👍
phosphorus	👍

Chocolate & mint yoghurt shake

Serves 2 full portions (easy to prepare)

Luscious, smooth, cool, fresh and chocolate. That's heaven in a glass!

100 g frozen chocolate yoghurt
25 to 50 ml crème de menthe or 1 tbsp mint extract
a splash of milk
chocolate shavings
a sprig of fresh mint

Scoop the frozen yoghurt into a blender. Add the crème de menthe and splash of milk and whiz until thick and smooth. Add more milk if too thick and a bit of ice if too thin. Dust with chocolate shavings and garnish with mint.

Each portion provides 2g protein and 170kcals.

nutrient	thumbs-up score
vitamin B12	👍

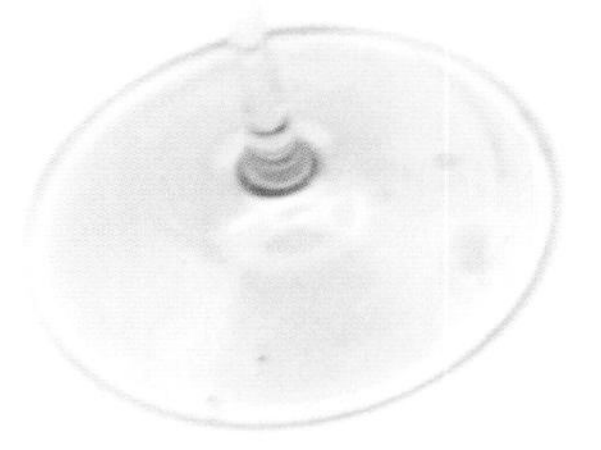

Apple à la mode ⚖

Serves 4 (easy to prepare)

This is a lovely, refreshing drink. It's like mom's apple pie in a glass (with an extra kick if you fancy).

100 ml (4 measures) dark rum
200 ml (8 measures) apple juice
4 small scoops of vanilla ice cream
2 cups ice
mint sprigs for garnish

Place all the ingredients in a blender and whip until smooth and creamy. Garnish with a small dollop of ice cream, a drizzle of rum and a mint sprig. Serve immediately.

Each portion provides 2g protein and 190kcals.

nutrient	thumbs-up score
vitamin C	👍

Frozen watermelon with ginger & lime ice ⚖

Serves 4 (easy to prepare)

It's fresh and zingy. For an adult version throw in a shot of vodka or mix with lashings of fizz. Ooh-ahh!

1 ripe round watermelon, halved & de-seeded
5 cm ginger, peeled & grated
juice of 2 limes
a pinch of sugar (optional)
zest of 1 lime, cut into fine strips for garnish
ice cubes
1 measure per serving of vodka (optional)

Put the flesh of the ½ watermelon, ginger and lime juice into a blender and blend until smooth. Add a touch of water if too thick. Check for sweetness, you may find you don't require any sugar. Pour into ice cube trays or lolly moulds and freeze.

When ready to serve, put the remaining watermelon into the blender and blend until smooth. Pop the fruit cubes into glasses, pour over with juice and garnish with a few lime shavings.

Serve immediately.

Each portion provides 1g protein and 80kcals.

nutrient	thumbs-up score
vitamin C	>👍👍👍👍

The basics & extras

Here are some traditional methods, many of which I've simplified to make things a bit easier.

Blind-bake

Partially baking a pastry crust before filling it ensures it won't go soggy. Line the crust with parchment and fill with ceramic baking beans (or uncooked beans or rice) and place in a medium oven for about 5 to 8 minutes. Do not allow it to colour. When cool, remove the beans and parchment.

Brown butter (beurre noisette)

Melt the butter in a pan over medium heat whisking until the solids turn brown. The flavour will become nutty. This is used frequently in baking and to give depth of flavour to sauces.

Clarified butter (ghee)

Put the butter into a heavy-bottomed saucepan and melt over medium heat. Skim off the foam. Carefully pour the clear liquid into a container and discard the whey (white solids).
Clarified butter keeps for several weeks in the refrigerator. It's good for sealing potted dishes and pâtés and is excellent for frying and basting as it can withstand high temperatures without burning.

Croutons

This is a great way to use those last bits of bread that you might otherwise discard.

bread of your choice, torn into bite-sized pieces
250 ml olive or sunflower oil
a handful of herbs de Provençe
salt & pepper

Pre-heat oven to 170ºCf. Add the herbs, salt and pepper to the oil then coat the bread pieces. Place the croutons in a baking dish (metal preferable) and bake for a few minutes, give them a shake to turn them over, finish baking for a few minutes until crisp but not too browned.

Dijon vinaigrette

Based on classic French cookery, you can add flavours such as crème fraîche, raspberries, honey or whatever suits your menu.

½ litre olive oil
1 tbsp Dijon mustard
a splash of balsamic vinegar
1 garlic clove, crushed
1 shallot, finely chopped
¼ cup fresh herbs or ⅛ cup herbs de Provençe
1 egg yolk
drop of sriracha
salt & pepper

English muffins – makes 8 muffins

300 g strong white bread flour, plus extra for flouring
6 g fast-action yeast (one sachet)
6 g salt
15 g caster sugar
15 g butter, softened & cut into small pieces
1 medium egg, lightly beaten
170 ml milk, or a bit more – enough to make a soft dough
a splash of sunflower oil for greasing
15 g semolina, plus extra for dusting

Tip the flour into a large mixing bowl. Sprinkle the yeast on one side of the flour and the salt into the other side. Add the sugar, butter, egg and milk then mix all the ingredients together to form a soft dough. Turn the mixture out of the bowl onto a lightly floured surface and knead for 10 minutes until soft, smooth and elastic. Lightly grease a large bowl with oil. Place the dough in the oiled bowl, cover and leave to prove for one hour or until doubled in size.

Dust a work surface with a mixture of semolina and flour. Tip the dough out onto the work surface and roll out to about 2.5 cm thick. Line 2 two baking trays with greaseproof paper then using a 9 cm straight-sided (or scone) cutter, cut out eight muffins. Place 4 muffins, evenly spaced apart, on each of the dusted baking trays. Dust the tops with semolina and prove for another 30 minutes.

Preheat a heavy-based frying pan to very low heat. Griddle the muffins for approximately 5 to 6 minutes, then flip over and griddle for another 5 to 6 minutes.

Hollandaise sauce

This is recipe is simplified from the traditional in order to be quick and easy to prepare.

325 ml clarified butter
2 egg yolks
2 tbsp cold water
1 tbsp of lemon juice
1 tsp of salt
drop of sriracha or pinch of cayenne pepper

In a clean glass bowl, whisk the egg yolks with 2 tbsp of cold water until frothy. Place the bowl over the pan of simmering water and whisk until thickened. Remove from the heat and whisk for a further minute to allow the eggs to cool then place back over the hot water but remove the pan from the heat. Slowly pour the melted butter into the egg yolk mixture continuously whisking. Add the remaining ingredients until blended together and as thick as you require.

Marinades

Marinades have 3 basic uses. They add flavour, moisture, and in some instances cook the meat. It is also a way of tenderising lesser cuts of meat. The acids introduced by ingredients such as citrus fruit, wine and vinegars cook raw meats such as carpaccio. Dry marinades introduce flavour by infusing spices and liquid marinades add moisture as well as flavour.

Mayonnaise & lemon mayonnaise

The type of oil will determine the richness. Use sunflower for light and olive for richer and peppery. This contains raw egg so must be kept refrigerated in a sealed container and used within 2 days. Add lemon to your taste.

1 egg yolk,
1 tbsp Dijon mustard
salt & freshly cracked black pepper, to taste
200 ml oil, sunflower or extra virgin olive oil
juice of 1 lemon, to taste (optional)

Whisk the egg yolk, mustard, salt and pepper until smooth and the salt is dissolved. Then whisk the oil a drop at a time until the mixture begins to emulsify. Continue to add in a steady but delicate stream until thick. For lemon mayonnaise, add lemon juice and final seasoning to taste.

Orange & almond tuilles

grated zest of 1 orange
½ cup sugar
3 tbsp flour
2½ tbsp freshly squeezed orange juice
100 g unsalted butter, melted
½ cup almond flakes

Place the orange zest and sugar in a bowl and rub together with your fingertips until the sugar absorbs the zest and becomes grainy and aromatic. Add the flour, juice and butter one by one, mixing to a dough with a spatula. Cover and refrigerate overnight.

Preheat the oven to 140°Cf.

Line an oven tray with baking paper and draw 6 circles of 8cm diameter on the paper. Drop half a teaspoon of the dough on to each circle, spread out with a spatula into the circular shape and sprinkle with a few almond flakes. Bake one sheet of tuiles at a time for 14 minutes or until the mixture spreads, bubbles and turns golden. Remove to another sheet of baking paper to cool then repeat with another batch until all the batter is used.

You can leave the tuiles flat or for curved, when still warm roll them around a rolling pin covered with baking paper to cool. Once cold, store in an airtight tin overnight. The batter will keep for up to 1 week refrigerated, but the tuiles will droop after about 24 hours so make them as close as possible to serving time.

Pasta

Serving portions are generally 50 to 75g per person for a side dish and 75 to 100g for a main. Pasta should always be added to the sauce rather than a sauce being poured onto the pasta.

Fresh egg pasta – serves 4

330 g strong flour (type 00 pasta flour)
3 eggs
1 yolk

Blend the flour, eggs and extra yolk together in a food processor until a dough is formed. Leave to rest in a refrigerator for 1 hour before use. Roll on a pasta machine until very thin and cut into desired thickness. If you don't have a pasta machine, a bit of elbow grease and a rolling pin work just as well.

Hang to dry until ready to use. (If making ravioli or tortellini you may want to roll the pasta sheet to make it a bit finer.)

When ready to use, bring a pan of salted water to a rolling boil, drop in the pasta and cook for approximately 2 minutes until just al dente. Don't overcook. Strain away the water and add to your desired sauce. If not using straightaway, plunge into a bowl of ice water until your sauce is ready.

For dry pasta, generously salt boiling water. When the pasta is al dente, strain and rinse thoroughly in cold water to stop the cooking process and remove excess starch. If the pasta is going to be standing for a few minutes before using, add a small amount of olive oil to prevent it from sticking. If you want to prepare the pasta well in advance, plunge into ice water as above.

Pastry

Short crust, puff and filo are all easily available ready-made. The recipes in this book are all easier to prepare using store-bought products but hand-made is always lovely. Here's an easy version to make short crust.

125 g plain flour
a pinch of salt
55 g butter, cubed or grated
2 to 3 tbsp cold water
cold hands

Mix the salt into the flour then, using your fingertips, rub the butter into the flour until you have coarse grains and no large lumps. Work quickly so it doesn't become greasy. Using a knife or pastry cutter, chop in enough water to bind the dough. Wrap the dough in clingfilm and chill for at least 10 minutes before rolling.

Pineapple, skin and eyes removed

Cut off the top and bottom and stand on end. A bread knife is a good tool for this. Notice that the 'eyes' run down in columns. Take off the skin in vertical slices, with a column of eyes in the centre, just deep enough to remove them. Follow the shape of the fruit. Remove any leftover eyes, tweezers work well, then cut in 1-inch thick slices.The core might be a bit hard and should also be removed.

Poaching eggs

Lay a flat plate on the bottom of a pan to prevent the eggs from sticking. Bring water to 80°C – just before the boil breaks the surface, (it helps to add a tbsp of white vinegar to the water). Gently crack and drop the egg into the water then give the water a gentle stir so the egg white gathers together. Cook for a couple minutes until the white is fully cooked and the yolk is still soft. Remove with a slotted spoon and drain on kitchen roll.

Raspberry coulis

Purée 115 g of raspberries and 1 tsp sugar in a blender with a splash of water. Pass through a sieve and set in the fridge until ready to use.

Rice

There are so many correct methods of preparing rice – many of them cultural, and if you don't have one, here is a simple solution. Gently wash the rice in cool running water then soak it for 1 hour. Cook the rice in boiling water for 10 minutes then rinse again with cold water. Place in an oven-proof dish and warm when ready to use. Wild rices will take about double the cooking time.

Roux

This is the basis for classic French cookery. Mix equal amounts of flour and butter over low heat stirring constantly with a wooden spoon. Keep the heat on the roux for a minute to allow the flour to fully cook. This can be set aside until you are ready to make your sauce. To continue making the sauce heat the roux and add small amounts of liquid such as milk for a bechamel, cheese or mustard sauce.

Sriracha, chilli paste and using chillies for seasoning

I have used a chilli sauce for decades called sriracha which is a 'Sambal Malaysian' variant. Used judiciously, it adds more lift, not heat to sauces and marinades. Others are: North African Harissa; Ancho, which is a Mexican variation; and Nam Prik Pao the Thai version made from roasted chillies. Generally, fresh chillies are less intense than dried. If you want full flavour but not so much heat remove the seeds.

Stock

The two things we usually don't have in home kitchens is time and capacity. Good stock is made over long periods with the refuse of main ingredients. Pre-prepared stock is available in many forms – canned, gels, cubes, powders. As a rule of thumb, the ones with less salt are worth seeking out.

Sugar syrup (also called simple syrup)

A mixture of 1 part granulated sugar and 1 part water (100 g sugar dissolved into 100 ml water).

Wasabi

Japanese horseradish. It is readily available in pre-made or powdered form. It adds flavour and a fair amount of heat.

Get moving

Equipment

Mobilisation

Endurance

Getting stronger

Balance and co-ordination

Stretches

Lymphoedema exercises

Thanks to The Pink Place, a special UK charity dedicated to supporting breast cancer patients, our Pink Place ladies: Maureen Brailey, Brenda Carrington, Barbara Hutton, Yvonne Houston, Ann Knight, Pam Monger, Lyn Nelson, Natasha Walsh, Chris Whiffin and in memory of Sylvia Holland, Cheryl Howard and Pam Love, all of whom gave us their time, enthusiasm and many smiles.

Online resource

Sarah created Wellbeing Exercise for people with problems (anything from arthritis and back pain to autoimmune conditions and cancer) who want to stay active, move better and be as healthy as possible.

As we explain earlier in the book (page 2) modern technology has enabled us to provide comprehensive online resources for cancer patients and Sarah now offers online exercise sessions, both one-to-one and for groups.

The science shows that everyone, no matter what restrictions they have, can benefit from exercise.

We believe that it can also be fun.

For more information go to our website www.chemocookeryclub.com/onlinehub or direct to Sarah's www.wellbeingexercise.co.uk

Equipment

Your own body is the heaviest weight you're likely to carry but some small and cheap pieces of equipment can be useful and add variety. Everything in this list can be picked up for less than £10 from High Street stores and discount outlets.

You can sit or stand on a balance cushion to strengthen your stomach and lower back and improve your balance.

A ***Swiss ball*** (also known as a gym ball, stability ball, Pilates ball or yoga ball) is a wonderful way to improve balance, your core muscles, stability and more. Plus it makes a comfortable seat. Bouncing gently on one for 15 minutes a day is a simple way to strengthen your pelvic floor, too.

Small ***hand weights*** (think 1 or 2 kilos) – also known as studio weights or dumbbells – provide a bit of extra resistance to strengthen muscles if you're finding small bottles of water or cans of veg too light. And ***ankle weights*** can make simple leg exercises more effective.

The best exercise ***mats*** are non-slip and nicely padded. You'll need one if you have wooden or tiled floors and want to do floor exercises.

Avoid ***resistance bands*** until you have completely healed, as it's difficult to know how much pressure you're exerting, which means you could hurt yourself. By all means add them to your routine later, if your medical team say it's OK.

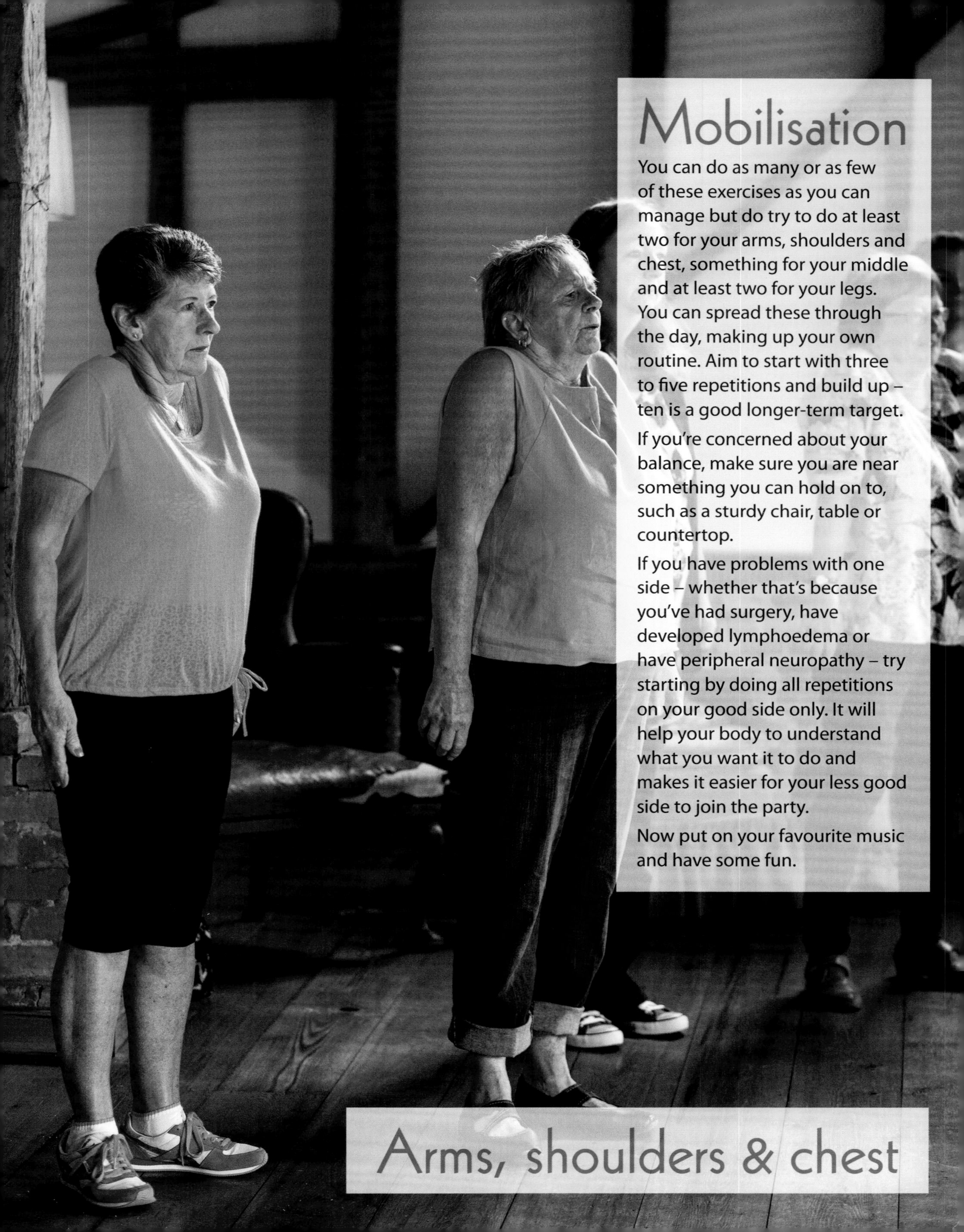

Mobilisation

You can do as many or as few of these exercises as you can manage but do try to do at least two for your arms, shoulders and chest, something for your middle and at least two for your legs. You can spread these through the day, making up your own routine. Aim to start with three to five repetitions and build up – ten is a good longer-term target.

If you're concerned about your balance, make sure you are near something you can hold on to, such as a sturdy chair, table or countertop.

If you have problems with one side – whether that's because you've had surgery, have developed lymphoedema or have peripheral neuropathy – try starting by doing all repetitions on your good side only. It will help your body to understand what you want it to do and makes it easier for your less good side to join the party.

Now put on your favourite music and have some fun.

Arms, shoulders & chest

Cossack arms

Sit or stand with your feet hip-width apart and cross your arms at upper chest height (a bit lower than in the photograph). If that's uncomfortable, go fingertip to fingertip or hold a CD case or small book between your hands. Keeping your hips totally still, rotate first to the left, then to the right. Inhale as you rotate out, exhale to engage your muscles as you return to the centre. The movement should come through your rib cage and mid-to-upper back, so don't cheat by only moving your arms.

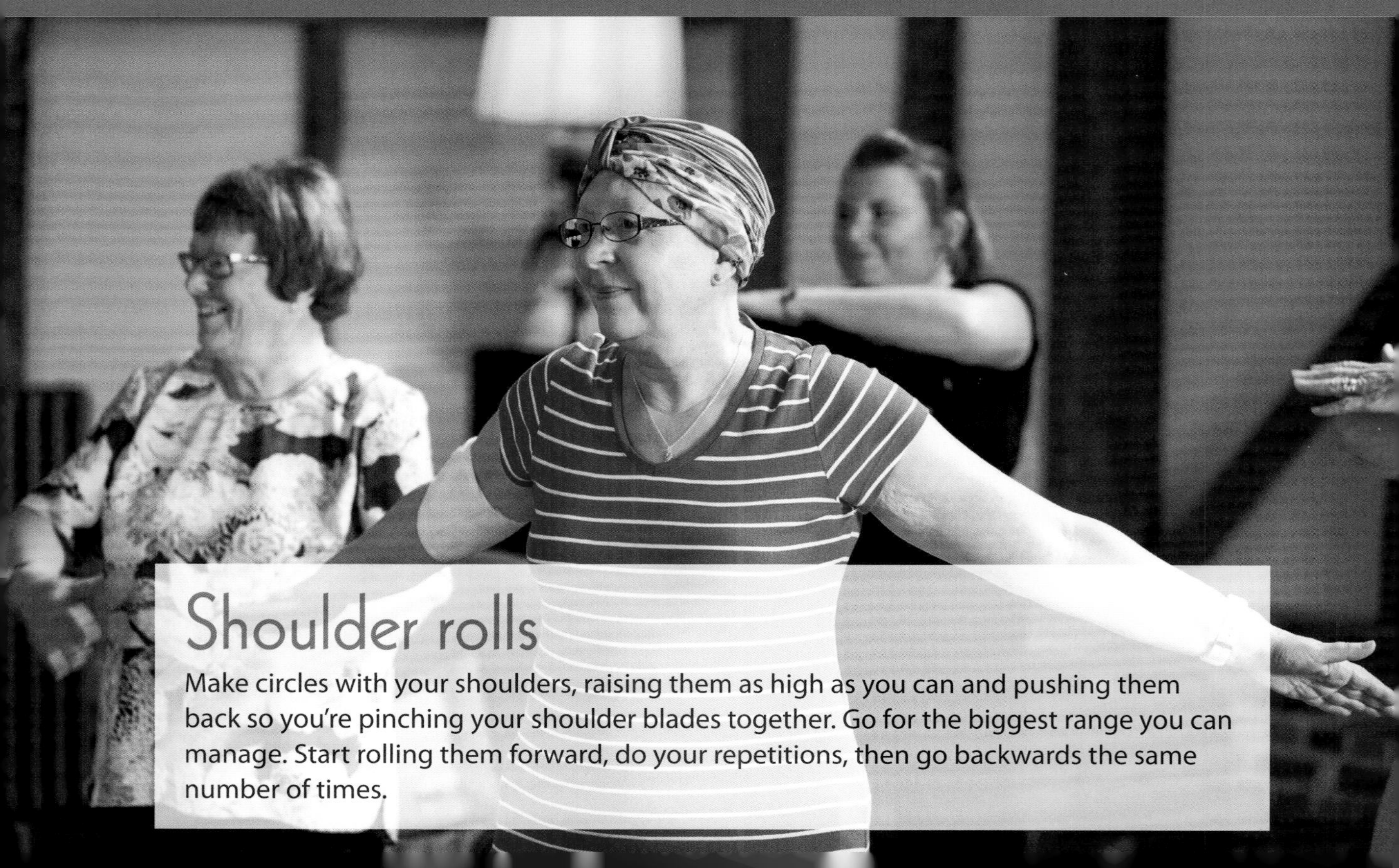

Shoulder rolls

Make circles with your shoulders, raising them as high as you can and pushing them back so you're pinching your shoulder blades together. Go for the biggest range you can manage. Start rolling them forward, do your repetitions, then go backwards the same number of times.

Arm flips

Let your arms hang loosely by your sides, then swing your forearms forward and up so your fingertips touch your shoulders. Swing them down and behind you to form an arrowhead shape, palms facing up.

Shoulder shrugs

Breathing in, raise your shoulders up high to your ears. As you exhale, bring them down again slowly, reaching your arms long down the side of your leg (or outside the arms of a chair), as if you're trying to bring your fingertips to the ground. Do this a few times, then try raising your shoulder as before and dropping them forcefully as you exhale. It can be helpful to make a whooshing noise as you do this.

Bird wings

Start with arms hanging by your sides and raise them both out sideways, like a bird spreading its wings. Try to keep your elbow soft and slightly higher than your forearms.

Insy Winsy Spider

You can do this up a wall or cupboard or go free-form. Start with your arms hanging down in front of you, then walk them up until your fingers are as high as you can go. If that's too tough, try walking your fingers out along a table or counter top at first. Eventually, you'll be able to go straight above your head.

Horizontal scissors

This will help to open up your chest. Start with your arms stretched out straight, at chest height if you can manage it, lower if not. Bring both arms in to cross horizontally over your chest, top hand on the lower elbow, bottom hand under the other elbow. Stretch back out to the sides again, then repeat with the other hand on top. Don't worry if you need to make the movements smaller at first – your range will improve with time and practice.

Middle

These will lengthen and loosen your waist and centre section.

If you have osteoporosis, please check with your medical team before trying these out. They may have other suggestions.

Torso rotations

Stand or sit with feet hip-width apart. If you're standing, let your arms hang down. If you're sitting, bend your elbows and raise your forearms until they're parallel to the ground. Then simply twist to your right, letting your arms fly as far as they can in that direction. Come back to the centre and go to the left. That's one repetition.

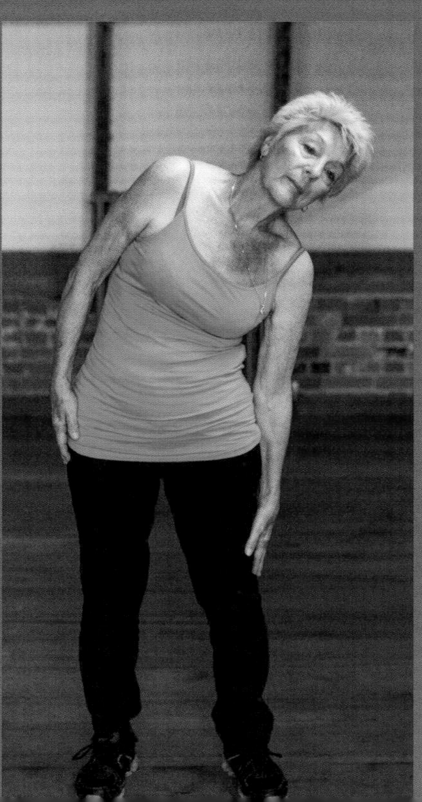

Side bends

Stand or sit with feet hip-width apart, arms by your sides. As you breathe in, lengthen up through your waist and sides (don't raise your shoulders), before reaching down on your right as far as you can as your breathe out. Try not to collapse your rib cage onto your hip or to bend forward – imagine you're sandwiched between two sheets of plate glass. Take it slowly, or you can use momentum to cheat. When you feel a good stretch down your side, pause and take a breath before returning to upright. Then repeat on the left. One bend each side is a single repetition. You can complete all the repetitions on one side and then swap, or alternate.

Legs & hips

High knees

March on the spot, raising your knees as high as you can. Take it slowly to start with and speed up as you become looser and stronger. You can try holding your hands out at waist height and tapping the raised knee with the opposite arm. You can do this sitting or standing.

Kick up your heels

This one eases out the front of your thighs. It's only possible if you can stand and you may want to position yourself sideways on to a solid piece of furniture or counter top, so you can hold on. Start with your feet hip-width apart and kick the heel of the outside leg towards your bottom. Try not to let the knee come forward – it should line up with the standing knee (although it almost certainly won't at first). Do all your repetitions on this side if you're holding on to something, then switch sides. If your balance is good enough not to hold on, you can alternate legs.

Pedalling

What it says on the tin: sitting or standing, press down on the ball of one foot while the heel rises, then switch sides, as if you're pedalling a bike. You can do a bit of this when you're sitting for a long time, to keep the blood circulating.

Heel digs

This one's good for taking the kinks out of your calves. Sitting or standing, stretch one leg out straight in front of you with your foot flexed and toes pointing up at the ceiling. Tap the floor with your heel, then swap sides and do the same again. That's one repetition.

Toe points

Sitting or standing, stretch one leg out straight in front of you, toe pointed, and tap the floor. Switch sides and do the same again. That's one repetition. Speed up as you get more confident. As your balance and confidence improves, you can try tapping your foot out to the back as well.

Draw a rainbow

This opens up your hips, which are probably tight if you've spent a lot of time sitting. Sitting or standing, feet slightly apart (and with something to hold onto if you're standing and wobbly), stretch one leg out straight in front of you then, keeping it straight, draw as big an arc as you can manage. Do all your repetitions on one side before repeating on the other side.

IMPORTANT NOTE:

If you have had a recent hip replacement, be very careful not to arc across the centre line of your body. Start with your foot pointed in front of your hip and arc round slowly and carefully behind you – again, don't go beyond the line of your hip.

Ask your medical team for advice if you are concerned.

Endurance

You know the expression, 'Use it or lose it?' That's what this is about. If you don't move enough, your heart will weaken, your muscles will melt away, you'll get breathless after the slightest exertion, your circulation will become sluggish and you'll generally feel much worse, both physically and mentally.

Walking, cycling, swimming, dancing, jogging, golf, table tennis, rebounding – just choose something you enjoy that gets your heart rate up and makes you slightly breathless. You'll get a natural high from the endorphins your body releases, which instantly makes you feel more positive. You'll maintain or increase your endurance, which means you'll cope better with everyday life. There are even theories that exercise makes treatment more effective, because your stronger circulation moves drugs round your body more efficiently and the by-products are whisked away more quickly.

Do talk to your medical team about the most appropriate way to build your endurance, as some activities may not be suitable for a few weeks or months. For example, you may be told not to use a public pool or gym if your immune system has been compromised by chemotherapy.

If you want advice on how to get the most out of a particular activity, the local branch of a cancer charity should also be able to help. Either way, you'll get lots of tips and the peace of mind that comes from knowing you're doing the right thing.

Measure your effort

The simplest way to assess how hard you need to work is to give yourself a scale from 1 to 10, where 1 is lying on the sofa and 10 is about to pass out. You need to be working moderately, which is somewhere around 3 to 6 out of 10, depending on your level of fitness, age and simply how you feel that day. You should be warm and slightly breathless, so you can still hold a conversation but not sing.

Ask yourself where you are on that 1 to 10 scale every five minutes or so. It will encourage you to think about how you feel, so you don't slack off or push yourself too hard.

How to walk well

The simplest, safest and cheapest thing you can do for yourself is walk. Here's how to get maximum benefit:

- start slowly and speed up when you begin to feel warmer and less tight
- make sure you land on your heel and roll through to the ball of your foot and your toes, which push you off into the next stride
- keep your shoulders relaxed and swing arms straight forward and back, keeping them parallel to your body (not crossing over the front)
- if you walk really fast, you should bend your arms so your forearms are parallel to the ground, with your hands loosely curled or flat, thumbs up, so they cut through the air like blades
- if you have a central line in one arm, go really easy on these movements – it may be better to let your arms hang naturally at your sides
- end your walk more slowly, until your breathing returns to normal.

Getting stronger

These exercises will help you to get stronger and prevent you from losing too much muscle.

That's important not only for everyday activities but also because muscle burns fat and keeps your metabolism revving.

You don't have to do all of these in one go. You might want to work your upper body on one day, your lower body on another and your back and stomach (your core) on a third, or pick one from each section and do a different selection on different days. Do include something that targets any part of your body that you know is weak. Aim to work on your strength three times a week, with at least one rest day in between sessions.

You should try to complete five repetitions of each exercise at first, gradually building up towards a target of ten.

Lower body

Calf raises

Good for calves and ankles, this couldn't be simpler. Stand with feet hip-width apart (you may want to be alongside a counter-top or piece of furniture for balance), then rise up onto the balls of your feet and slowly lower back to the ground.

Chair rises

These strengthen your legs, stomach and back muscles so getting up from a chair, sofa or bed is easier. Simply position yourself fairly near the edge of a solid chair or box, feet hip-width apart and arms crossed over your chest. Then stand up in one strong movement. Push your bottom back and sit down once more, just touching the chair, then stand up again.

IMPORTANT NOTE: Ensure that the chair will not slip by placing it against a wall or a solid piece of furniture.

Pick-up

We all need to bend down and pick stuff up from the floor, whether we've got shopping bags to carry or have simply dropped a hankie. This exercise shows the safest way to do it, without hurting your lower back. At the same time, it works the back of your legs, your hip, stomach and lower back muscles. I suggest you do this with a large milk container or a bag containing a few cans of veg – you can increase the number of cans when you're more confident.

Place the object you're going to lift on a low step or stool. Stand fairly close to, feet hip-width apart and arms hanging loosely by your side. Hinge at the hips, pushing your bottom out and keeping your chest high – don't round your back. Let your arms come down towards the object and bend your knees slightly. They should not come further forward than your toes. Grasp the object and, keeping your arms long, stand up again, using the power in your legs and bottom, not your arms. You've just done what weightlifters know as a deadlift and my clients call Comedy Bum, because you really do have to stick it out quite a way. As you get used to the movement, you can place whatever you're lifting on the floor – as always, start cautiously and progress slowly.

If you have osteoporosis, please check with your medical team before trying this.

Upper body

Bicep curls

The front of your arms are your lifting gear, so strengthen them with bicep curls. Sit or stand with feet hip-width apart, arms long, holding an appropriate weight with your palms facing up (small bottles of water or cans of tomatoes will do to start with). Brace your stomach and clench your bottom so you don't rock backwards. Keeping your elbows tight to your side, so your upper arms don't move, breathe out as you curl your forearms up to the front of your shoulders. Pause for a breath, then slowly lower back to the start.

Wall press-ups

Good for your chest, backs of arms, core and balance, this is a classic exercise that tones and strengthens. Stand a few feet from a wall and put your hands on it at shoulder level, so your body forms a diagonal. Be careful not to let your hips sag down and don't stick your bottom out, either – you should be in a straight line. Bend your elbows to lower yourself towards the wall as you inhale and straighten them to push back up to the starting position as you exhale.

Chair holds

The muscles at the back of your upper arm, the triceps, help you to lever yourself up from the bath, bed or sofa. Exercise them by sitting on the edge of a stable chair or bench (you may need to position it against a wall, so it doesn't move) with your arm by your sides, holding the edge of the seat. Make sure your wrists are straight and your knuckles point forwards. Then shift your weight forwards, so your arms are straight and your upper and lower legs form a right angle

You may need to experiment with the distance your feet are from the chair to get this right but it's important, or you could stress your knees. Then lift yourself back onto the chair again. Try to push upwards, rather than straight back. When your get good at this, you can lower your body slightly by bending your elbows before you push back up.

IMPORTANT NOTE:
Make sure that the chair or bench cannot slip backwards by wedging it against a wall.

Shoulder circles

These are surprisingly hard work but brilliant at improving shoulder strength and mobility. Sit or stand with your arms out to the sides at shoulder level, or as high as you can manage, palms facing down. Make sure your arms are at the same height. Then make small circles with your arm – try 3-5 in each direction. Then flip your hands so your palms face up and make the circles again.

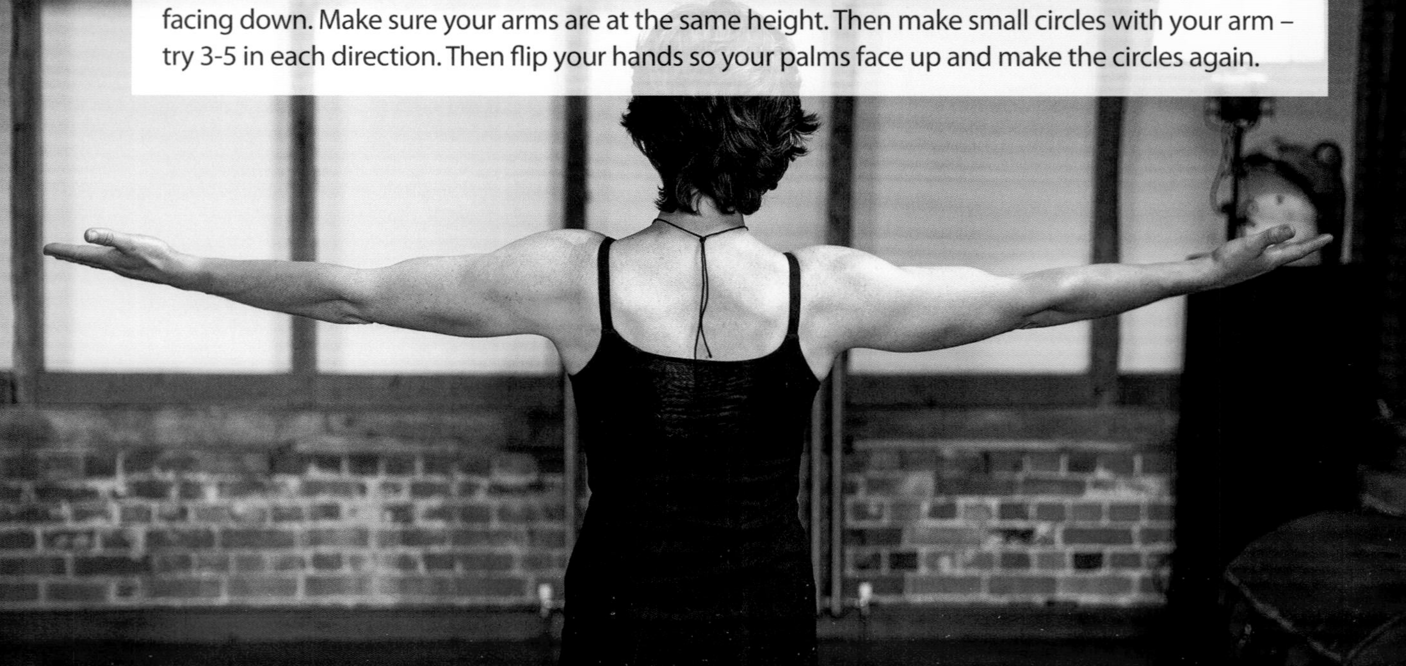

The core

Cat cow

This classic yoga and Pilates move is wonderful for mobilising and strengthening your back and improving balance. Start on all fours, with your hands directly beneath your shoulders, palms flat and fingers pointing forwards, and knees directly below your hips. Take a deep breath in and, as you exhale, tuck your chin about half-way towards your chest, push your tailbone down towards the floor and curl your pelvis under as you arch your back up like a cat, one vertebra at a time. You'll finish this part of the movement with your head heavy, looking back at your thighs. Take another big breath and, as you exhale, push your tailbone back and uncurl your spine as you return to your starting position.

If your lower back doesn't pinch, you can let it drop a little and push your bottom up (don't do this if you have lower back problems).

If your wrists hurt when kneeling on all fours, you can try making fists instead of having your hands flat on the floor. Or move your knees slightly further back.

If you can't get down to the floor, your can put your hands on a sturdy table or kitchen countertop and start with your back flat and your knees and feet in line with your hips. Then curl up and back as in the previous instructions.

Seated leg lift with rotation

Your stomach, sides, lower back and front of thigh work in this exercise. Start sitting near the front of a firm chair, feet roughly hip-width apart. The easiest way to do this is to hold the side of the chair and lift one leg at a time until it is parallel to the floor. Then try without holding on. When that gets easy, put your hands to the side of your head (or cross them over your chest) and twist your body away from the raised leg. Whichever variant you choose, one raise of each leg is a single repetition. If you have osteoporosis, stick with the leg raises and leave out the rotation.

Standing back extensions

Strengthen your lower back and improve your balance and range of motion in your shoulders by standing a few feet away from a wall with both hands resting on it, so your body forms a diagonal line. The closer you stand, the easier it is. Arc one arm backwards, turning slightly and keeping your eye on the hand. You can twist as much or as little as is comfortable. You should feel the muscles in your side, lower back and upper part of the bottom working. Then return to the start and turn to the other side. One movement to each side is one repetition.

Standing crunch

Stand with your back against a wall for balance (you can keep your fingertips on the wall as well if you need to) and raise one knee as high as you can, tensing your stomach muscles as you go. Hold for a breath, then put your foot down and swap legs. That's one repetition.

Balance & co-ordination

Pick one of these to slot in every day and your balance could actually improve, rather than deteriorating. If you're nervous or very wobbly, get someone to stand beside you, so you can hang onto them if you need to. Or do these alongside a wall, which you can prop on if necessary.

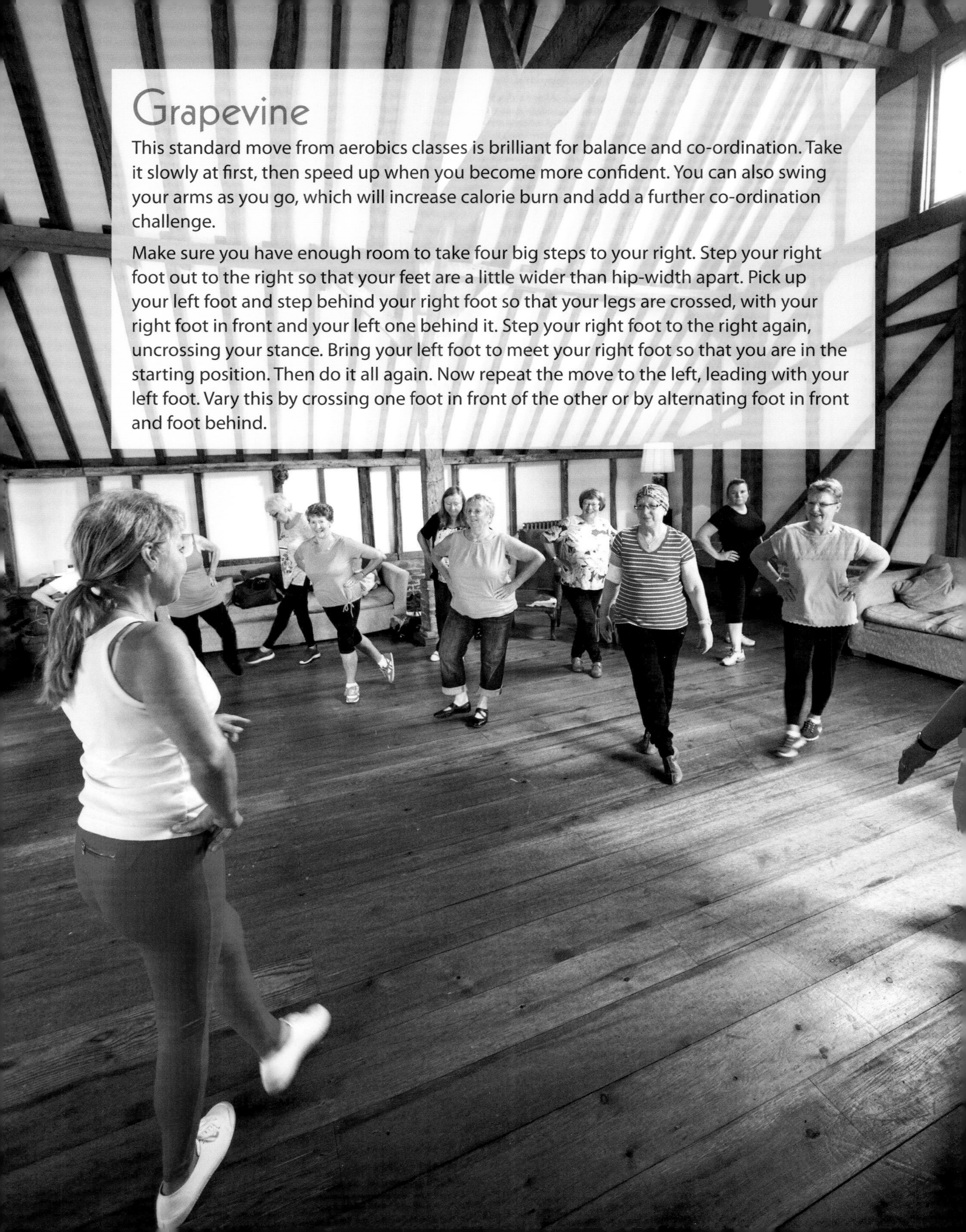

Grapevine

This standard move from aerobics classes is brilliant for balance and co-ordination. Take it slowly at first, then speed up when you become more confident. You can also swing your arms as you go, which will increase calorie burn and add a further co-ordination challenge.

Make sure you have enough room to take four big steps to your right. Step your right foot out to the right so that your feet are a little wider than hip-width apart. Pick up your left foot and step behind your right foot so that your legs are crossed, with your right foot in front and your left one behind it. Step your right foot to the right again, uncrossing your stance. Bring your left foot to meet your right foot so that you are in the starting position. Then do it all again. Now repeat the move to the left, leading with your left foot. Vary this by crossing one foot in front of the other or by alternating foot in front and foot behind.

Heel-to-toe walk

Walk in an absolutely straight line, placing one foot directly in front of the other, with the heel of the front foot touching the toes of the back foot.

Heel walks

Walk normally on your heels. When you've mastered this, try doing the heel-to-toe walk on your heels.

Standing on one leg

The length of time you can stand on one leg is a measure of strength and balance, and a mark of your body age – luckily, you can improve very quickly with regular practice. It also works your legs and bottom, so you'll be able to walk further, climb stairs better and get up more easily.

Stand next to something solid, like a kitchen countertop, in case you wobble. While you build your confidence and muscles, you can rest your fingertips on it for balance. Stand on one leg for as long as you can, then swap over. Try doing this every time you're waiting for the kettle to boil. Aim to reach at least 30 seconds on each leg.

When standing on one leg gets easy, try pointing the toe of your raised leg forward, out to the side and back. Then try it with your foot flexed, toes pointing to the ceiling

Stretches

You can slot a few of these in at any point in the day if one part of your body is feeling especially tight or tense but a stretching session is particularly relaxing at bedtime. A warm bath or shower beforehand will loosen your muscles in advance.

Pick stretches that target your tightest parts, making sure to include something for your lower body as well as your arms and torso. Aim to hold each of these for up to 30 seconds – you should feel mild tension but no pain. Stop immediately if you feel a sharp twinge. Remember to breathe slowly and deeply throughout – don't hold your breath.

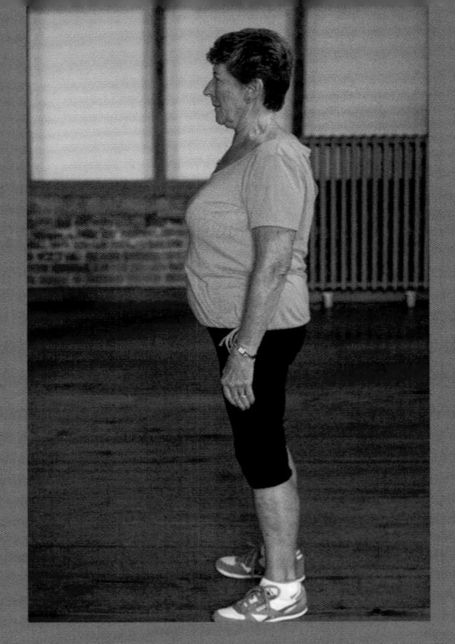 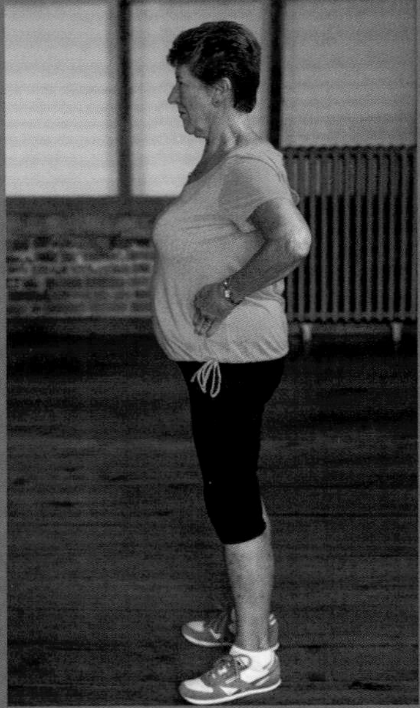 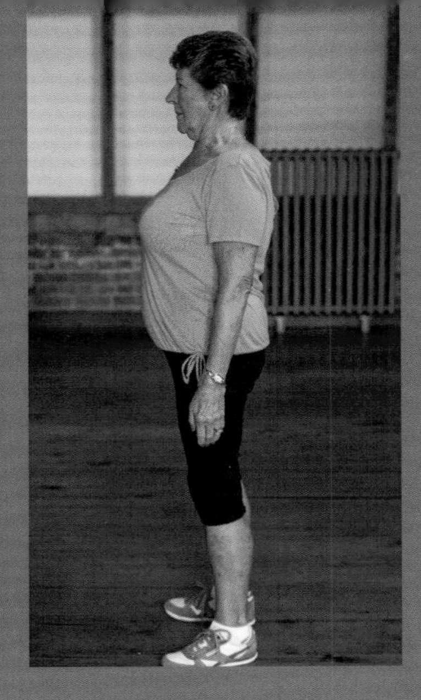

Stand up straight

This is worth doing first thing in the morning as well as last thing at night. If you do it in front of a mirror, you'll see yourself grow taller. You'll also breathe more deeply, flooding your body with oxygen.

Stand or sit with feet hip-width apart and let your arms dangle loosely. Point your tailbone down to the floor without clenching your bottom (don't tuck your pelvis under more then a very little), then tighten up the muscles in the lower part of your stomach, between your hip bones (still no clenching of your bottom, please). Take three long, deep breaths in through your nose and out through your mouth. On the third exhalation, scoop your rib cage up away from your waist, preferably without raising your shoulders. Then do a half shoulder roll backwards, flop your arms backwards and forwards loosely and lengthen your collar bones.

Neck stretch

Turn your head as far as is comfortable to the right and hold. Return slowly to the centre and do the same to the left.

Shoulder stretch

Place one arm diagonally across your torso, hand pointing down. Hook the other hand behind it above your elbow and pull until you feel a stretch. Then do the same on the other side. Do not pull across your elbow – you could hurt the joint. If you want a stronger stretch, hook your hand around your forearm rather than upper arm.

Calf stretch

Stand with the balls of your feet on the edge of a bottom step or stair, holding on to the banister. Let your heels drop downwards until you feel a stretch in the back of your calves.

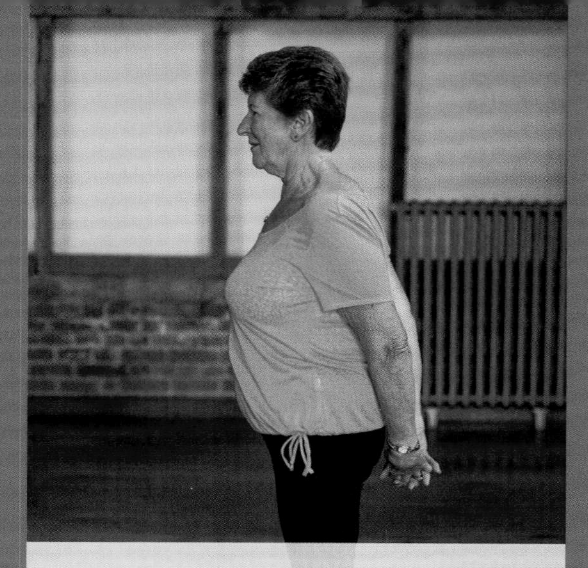

Chest stretch

Stand or sit with your arms behind your back, fingers laced together behind your bottom. Push down rather than out.

W stretch

Raise your arms so they form a W shape, then slowly bring our elbows in towards your body and hold. You should feel your shoulder blades pulling down and inward, towards the centre of your back.

Hug a tree

This will loosen your upper back. Drop your chin to your chest and make a circle of your arms at chest level, fingers laced loosely together, as if you were hugging a tree. Then turn your hands out so your palms are facing forward and push your hands away from your body. This will loosen your upper back but is best avoided if you have osteoporosis in your neck.

Buttock stretch

If you spend a lot of time sitting, the muscles that move your hips get tight, which makes it harder to move easily and can even lead to sciatica. This will help – but go easy, as it's quite intense. Sit near the front of a firm chair and cross one leg over the other, resting one ankle just above the opposite knee. Lean forward until you feel the stretch. Then swap sides.

Avoid this if you've had a recent hip replacement – check with your medical advisors first if you have any doubts.

Front of thigh stretch

Kneel on your bed – hold onto the headboard for balance. Then let your weight sink backwards, as your bottom comes towards your heels. If you find kneeling uncomfortable, you can stand beside a piece of furniture and hold on lightly. Lift your outside foot back towards your bottom and pull it gently upwards – you can hold your ankle, foot or heel to do this.

Back of leg stretch

Lie on your back on your bed – you may want a small pillow under your neck, so you aren't tilting your head back. Bend both knees and raise one foot into the air, keeping it straight. Reach behind your thigh (or shin, if you're very flexible) and pull gently towards you. Then do the other side.

Lymphoedema exercises

Sit upright, with your arm comfortably resting in your lap or on a pillow or cushion. Then run through these, aiming to do each exercise ten times.

- make a fist with your hand, then open it and spread your fingers wide
- place your palm face down, bend your hand backwards from the wrist so that your wrist stays on the cushion and your fingers point to the ceiling. Then move your hand back down so your fingers are pointing to the floor
- with your arm straight on the cushion and your palm facing up, lift your arm up until your hand touches your shoulder
- reach your hand behind your back so that the back of your hand is touching your bottom, then lift your hand up your back as far as you can without discomfort
- lift your arm up so that your hand is behind your head if you can – just get as far as possible and keep on trying.

Glossary

al dente – pasta cooked so it is still firm

arugula – rocket

aubergine – eggplant

bain marie – a pan containing hot water that smaller pans are put into for slow cooking

beurre noisette (brown butter) – butter that has cooked long enough to make it the colour of nuts. Its rich flavour is used in classic French sauces and gravies. Unsalted butter is best.

beetroot – beet

blind-bake – the process of baking a pie crust or other pastry without the filling

bundt tin – traditional ring-shaped European cake tin

Camargue red rice - a nutty wild rice from the Camargue region in the South of France

caster sugar – refined sugar. Called 'fine or 'superfine' in America. When using sugar for jellies or other fine desserts where the sugar is melted in liquid, you can use granulated sugar as it is 'cleaner'

celeriac – celery root

chiffonade – a slicing technique where green leaves and herbs are tightly rolled then sliced to create fine ribbons

chips – in the UK these are 'fries' and chips are called 'crisps'

cinder toffee – honeycomb

cook without colour – sauté until softened but not browning

coriander – cilantro

courgette – zucchini

crème fraîche – lightly soured cream

cuticle – the protective skin-like coating on foods that seal in the moisture or liquid such as eggs, citrus fruit and peppers. It's Nature's way of sealing out bacteria and preserving freshness

deglaze the pan – adding liquid (stock or wine) to a pan to loosen food particles to make a sauce

double cream – heavy cream or whipping cream. It is generally higher in fat content than 'whipping cream' so quickly turns to butter if over-whipped.

goujons – a small strip of fish or chicken

granita – a semi-frozen dessert made from sugar, shaved ice and flavourings

grill – broil or salamander

herbs de Provençe – dried basil, oregano, rosemary, sarriette & thyme

Italian tomatoes – Roma or pomodoro tomatoes

jelly – gelatine dessert 'jello' or jellied condiment

julienne – finely sliced slivers

knob of butter – a generous tablespoon

lemonade – in the UK this is typically a fizzy drink (similar to Sprite). In the US it is fresh lemon juice mixed with sugar and water

Maldon salt – flaked sea salt from east of England. When seasoning raw meats and fish use coarse salt as fine table salt will leech into the meat

marrow – a large squash, like a courgette (zucchini)

mirin – a Japanese rice wine similar to Sake with lower alcohol and higher natural sugar content, typically used in soups, marinades and dressings

parchment – waxed paper

pudding – dessert (in English, pudding is a broad term for dessert and also sweet or savoury steamed dishes such as Yorkshire pudding. In America, it is usually identified with a sweet creamy dessert)

pumpkin – squash (such as butternut) . In Australia, pumpkin is a generic term for all squash but frequently refers to butternut.

quenelle – a 3-sided oval shape of soft components such as ice cream or pâté

roux – flour and fat cooked together to form the basis for sauces. The traditional fat is butter, but for less energy-dense and for vegan requirements, other oils can be used

season to taste – salt & pepper

spring onions – green onions or scallions (a larger version)

sriracha – a chilli sauce originating from Malaysia. Available in most supermarkets

stock – broth

tenderloin – fillet

tomato purée – tomato paste

wild mushrooms –there are a vast majority of wild edible mushrooms including: chanterelles, chestnut, field, porcini, trompette, oyster and giant puffball. Many varieties of these are sold as responsibly grown exotic mushrooms in supermarkets. The most important thing is that you are absolutely certain that any wild mushroom you use has been positively identified as safe and edible.

Conversion chart

Liquid measures	
15ml	½ fl oz
20ml	¾ fl oz
25ml	1 fl oz
35ml	1¼ fl oz
40ml	1½ fl oz
50ml	2 fl oz
60ml	2¼ fl oz
65ml	2½ fl oz
85ml	3 fl oz
100ml	3½ fl oz
120ml	4 fl oz
150ml	5 fl oz (¼ pint)
175ml	6 fl oz
200ml	7 fl oz
250ml	8 fl oz
275ml	9 fl oz
300ml	10 fl oz (½ pint)
325ml	11 fl oz
350ml	12 fl oz
375ml	13 fl oz
400ml	14 fl oz
450ml	15 fl oz (¾ pint)
475ml	16 fl oz
500ml	17 fl oz
550ml	18 fl oz
575ml	19 fl oz
600ml	20 fl oz (1 pint)
750ml	1¼ pints
900ml	1½ pints
1 ltr	1¾ pints
1.2 ltr	2 pints
1.25 ltr	2¼ pints
1.5 ltr	2½ pints
1.6 ltr	2¾ pints
1.75 ltr	3 pints
2 ltr	3½ pints

Solid measures	
5g	⅛ oz
10g	¼ oz
15g	½ oz
20g	¾ oz
25g	1 oz
40g	1½ oz
50g	2 oz
65g	2 ½ oz
75g	3 oz
90g	3½ oz
100g	4 oz (¼ lb)
120g	4½ oz
135g	4¾ oz
150g	5 oz
165g	5½ oz
175g	6 oz
185g	6½ oz
200g	7 oz
215g	7½ oz
225g	8 oz (½ lb)
250g	9 oz
275g	10 oz
300g	11 oz
350g	12 oz (¾ lb)
375g	13 oz
400g	14 oz
425g	15 oz
450g	16 oz (1 lb)
550g	1¼ lb
750g	1½ lb
1kg	2¼ lb
1.25kg	2½ lb
1.5kg	3½ lb
1.75kg	4 lb
2kg	4½ lb
2.25 g	5 lb

Linear measures	
3mm	⅛ inch
5mm	¼ inch
1cm	½ inch
2cm	¾ inch
2.5cm	1 inch
3cm	1 ⅛ inch
4cm	1 ½ inch
4.5cm	1 ¼ inch
5cm	2 inches
6cm	2 ½ inches
7.5cm	3 inches
9cm	3½ inches
10cm	4 inches
13cm	5 inches
15cm	6 inches
18cm	7 inches
20cm	8 inches
23cm	9 inches
25cm	10 inches
28cm	11 inches
30cm	12 inches (1 ft)

Liquid measures

2.25 ltr	4 pints
2.5 ltr	4½ pints
2.75 ltr	5 pints
3.4 ltr	6 pints
3.9 ltr	7 pints
4.5 ltr	8 pints
5 ltr	9 pints

Solid measures

2.5 kg	5½ lb
2.75 kg	6 lb
3 kg	7 lb
3.5 kg	8 lb
4 kg	9 lb
4.5 kg	10 lb
5 kg	11 lb
5.5 kg	12 lb

Oven temperatures

Gas	C	C fan	F	Oven Temp
¼	110	90	225	very cool
½	120	100	250	very cool
1	140	120	275	cool or slow
2	150	130	300	cool or slow
3	160	140	325	warm
4	180	160	350	moderate
5	190	170	375	medium hot
6	200	180	400	fairly hot
7	220	200	425	hot
8	230	210	450	very hot
9	240	220	275	very hot

Index